IN SEARCH OF SLOVAKIA

IN SEARCH OF SLOVAKIA

by

HENRY BAERLEIN

BRENTANO'S LTD.

NEW YORK   LONDON   PARIS

First Published 1929.

*Made and Printed in Great Britain by Ebenezer Baylis and Son, Limited,
The Trinity Press, Worcester.*

TO JANOS RADVANSZKY

MY DEAR JANOS,

You and your ancestors have lived for eight hundred years in a Slovak castle, so that you have no doubt inherited a great knowledge of Slovak affairs ; and I, a stranger, instead of writing this book should have left it for you to accomplish. But you will not, I feel sure, reveal any of my inaccuracies, exaggerations, lacunæ, obscurities and so forth, since you have a kindly disposition. When a damsel of eighteen months—that is to say, two and a half years your junior—was tugging away at your abundant fair locks and you were asked if you permitted this, " One should permit a lady," you replied, " to do anything." The other day you were proposing to examine more closely a herd of sheep, but as you started to walk across the field your mother spoke a word of warning. " They do not know you," she said. Then with a ceremonial bow you told them that your name is Janos Radvanszky. " And now," you said, " they know me." It may be more difficult to acquire a knowledge of Slovakia ; yet, I repeat, you will be indulgent. And as, in this respect, I feel more certain of you than of other people, it is to you that I dedicate this account of my journey.

Always your friend,

H. B.

IN SEARCH OF SLOVAKIA

CHAPTER I

" A HAPPY journey! A happy journey to you! "
exclaimed the porter of the hotel, as he was about to
leave my room.

Considering that I had just arrived, which no one
knew better than himself, as he had brought my luggage
on a wheelbarrow from the station, I did not precisely
grasp why, except if he was speaking in a general kind
of way, he should wish me a happy journey.

There was nothing mysterious about his appearance :
he was squarely built and with a face of no distinction.
Perhaps he had only uttered the words in a fit of
absent-mindedness. And yet there might be something
here which would repay investigation. In that case
it would be fatal if I were to ask him crudely what he
meant by his good wish. Once or a thousand times in
our lives we stand at the frontier of a dark country ;
we shall never cross that frontier if we are un-
worthy.

How was I to retain the porter ?

" You have been having much rain ? " I asked.

" Oh yes," he said.

" I noticed some large puddles on the footpath." He had circumnavigated them with great skill.

" I am glad that you have come," he said with a very amiable smile. " Turčiansky Svaty Martin* is an interesting place. Over there," he said, pointing through the window, " that is the museum. A lot of things have happened in Turčiansky."

I knew—indeed, that was why I had to come—of the fame of this little town which had for centuries been the capital, as it were, of a country which did not exist. The Slovaks had for about ten centuries been included in the Hungarian Kingdom ; and when in 1918 they, with their kinsmen the Czechs, achieved their freedom the capital, it was decided, could not be the rather remote Turčiansky. This dignity was conferred upon Bratislava, a much larger town upon the Danube. So Bratislava became the capital of Slovakia, with Prague the capital of the whole Czechoslovakian Republic.

" If you are going to tell me some of the things that have happened here," I said, " then you had better sit down."

" Well, what I remember myself," quoth the porter, " is that of October, 1918. They all assembled here and there was not room for half of them. Then they settled to be in Czechoslovakia."

---

*That is to say : Turčiansky St. Martin.   The first word is pronounced Turchiansky.

" But where else could they be ? "

" Where. . . ." The good fellow seemed to be a little confused, even as in October 1918 the dissolving Austro-Hungarian Empire. At that time National Councils were being formed everywhere, one for example at Turčiansky, whose object it was to establish for Slovakia some central authority corresponding with the National Council of the Czechs, the inhabitants of Bohemia and Moravia, which was set up in Prague. But, of course, the union of Czechs and Slovaks had been prepared during the war by their collaboration outside Austria-Hungary, when they created the Czechoslovak legions that fought in Russia, France and Italy, while the Czechoslovak National Council had its headquarters in Paris. But the Czechoslovak idea had been mooted long before the war when—to speak of one or two of its champions—Kollár the poet and Šafařik the historian, who flourished about a hundred years ago, dreamed of the free cultural development of Czechs and Slovaks. So closely akin are these two branches of the great Slav family that up to 1860 they employed the same literary language ; it was only then that one of the Slovak dialects was adopted as the Slovak language. And now the political union is gradually bringing about the return to one language, the Czechoslovak language.

" In October of 1918," said the porter, " I was here at Turčiansky, but not in this hotel. I was in a little one which is called The Green Tree. It is near the

Jewish and Catholic cemeteries. That is why the name
of the street is the Street of Death."

"Do you mean to say that there are people in this
town who are satisfied to have an address of that kind
on their notepaper ? "

"I have never asked them," he said. "But it is
nice to think that I was here in October of 1918. It is
like being a man in history. Would you like me to tell
you about it ? "

I said that I would like nothing better.

"You can unpack your things at the same time,"
quoth he. "Let me open that bag with all the labels
on." He was wreathed in smiles as he regarded them.
"Well," he resumed, "as I said before, I wish you a
happy journey ! "

"Thank you very much," I said. "I wish you would
go with me. I shall have to walk to Orava and Ružomberok and other places. The luggage can stay here
until I come back. I have heard so much about
Slovakia," I said, "that I want to see it for myself.
If it is true what some people say, then it must be a
second and worse Armenia, because I believe the
Armenians were only oppressed by the Turks, whereas
in this country of yours the Czech oppresses the Slovak
and——"

"Is that so ? " said the porter.

I begged him not to interrupt me. "And the
Slovak," I said, "oppresses the Hungarian, the
Magyar. At all events that is what some people say.

How could I control their statements if I were to travel through the land by rail or car ? That is why I mean to walk. And there are others who declare that Slovakia is a happy province ! "

" If only I could go with you," said the amiable fellow, " then my street-barrow could take the luggage. It is a pity that I can't go. It is a great pity." Then, of a sudden, the gloom passed from his countenance. " We can go to the museum," he said. " I have nothing else to do for the moment."

The proprietor of the hotel, a melancholy Serb with red-rimmed eyes behind his glasses, looked at us as we went through the hall, but only sighed.

" This gentleman wants to have someone," said the porter, " who will walk with him to other parts of the land. Now we are going to the museum."

The Serb nodded. " Well, yes," he remarked. " Someday I must go there myself. But this," he confided to me, " is a dead little town."

In the hope of rendering him more cheerful I told him of one that is probably more dead, namely the town of Zara, that erstwhile capital of Dalmatia, which the Allies in their folly had bestowed on the Italians, so that this tiny enclave on Yugoslav soil has seen its population diminish from thirty-five thousand to one fifth of that number. I told him of the empty streets and of the empty port, and how the authorities had conveyed a large crane from Italy, had erected it on the harbour and left it there in idleness, so that the people said it was not meant to lift the merchandise out of the ships, but to raise the morale of Zara.

" It must be unpleasant," said the Serb, " for the people who live there."

" Many of them die," I told him, " for they attempt —it is about the only commerce left—to smuggle cigarettes across the boundary into Yugoslavia. But as your gendarmes appear to be selected for their markmanship, it is quite dangerous."

The Serb rubbed his hands together and was good enough to tell me that I had encouraged him. He thought that there might be improvements in Turčiansky, so that he would not have to shut up his fine hotel.

" That is what I always tell them at the station," said the porter, " that it is a fine hotel. Besides I tell them it is the only one."

" You are a good boy," said the Serb, " but when you say it is the only one. . . ."

" They do not know, or else they would not ask me," said the porter.

" So, so," said the Serb. " Well, I give you leave to go to the museum with this gentleman. I have been told that a court of justice is to be installed here and a regiment—God send them. If they come I will not be obliged to close the house. Now will you make a note for me," he said, " of what is interesting over there and someday I will go there too."

The porter, as we went across the road, said that he

could not tell me anything about his master's tastes. But in our progress round the various crowded rooms of the museum I discovered that all reasonable tastes are catered for—there is, to take one item, a skull of which the jaws are fastened to each other by two padlocks. Possibly, it is surmised, this woman was declared to be a witch whose arts were exercised upon a cow, so that it gave no milk. The punishment was not so very inappropriate, because the padlocked witch would be unable to take any nourishment save milk or water. Then they have in the museum formidable combs—in Detva and some other regions there are men who, down to this day, wear long hair, while some of them affect the pigtail, of which three or four hang from their heads. The prehistoric weapons and utensils are, of course, non-Slovak, since that people had not yet descended, for their joy and grief, upon this land. In the collection of stuffed animals there is a calf not noticeably Slovak, for it has two heads and that occurs, no doubt, in other countries. What are we to say about the cock with horns ? It is a comely specimen. But was he always furnished with these two unusual excrescences because his mother had been startled by some big horned animal, perhaps a goat, or did they sprout when the poor cock was shamefully deceived by one of his own wives ?

When we returned to the hotel we told the Serb what we had seen and he repeated that he certainly must go someday to the museum.

" It is curious," he said, " that you only come here for a day—"

" But possibly I will stay several days," I told him.

He did not conceal it from me that he was surprised. " We only have a cinema," he said, " one evening every week."

" But I like your hotel and I have to prepare for my walk through Slovakia."

He shrugged his shoulders. " Anyhow, it is one of the cleanest. We are always washing it. I believe when you are in some others in Slovakia you will think of me. In several of the towns they are constructing new hotels. The world is being made much cleaner. In my own town, which is Belgrade—you have been to Belgrade ? Well, I have received a letter from a friend, a business-man—he tries to make loans from other countries, England, Holland and so on, to Yugoslavia. He says that there have been so many incidents in all the streets of Belgrade, as there is a regulation—it was made a little time ago—to stop the citizens from spitting. There are some officials, male and female, not in uniform, who walk about the streets and catch the people when they spit. A fine has to be paid—one hundred and fifty dinars, which is about eleven shillings of your money—and a receipt is given. But there are difficulties. For example most of the Ministers and ex-Ministers and the Deputies claim that they are immune and they decline to pay. And many of the other people object. It is an evil time, they argue, when one loses more and more of one's liberties. A certain official wrote in his report : ' To-day throughout my district there have been eleven people who spat, nine of them on the street, and two of them on me.' Yes," said the Serb to the porter, " what do you want to say ? "

" Nothing, nothing. Please go on," said that person.

" There was another group of people who were glad, it seems. They were discussing politics, the crisis—we are always in a crisis—and they were seated just outside the Café Balkan. They were spitting heavily. And one of those officials, a young woman, came that way. She was not then on duty, so that she could not inflict a fine. But she stood there, outside the Balkan, and she lectured all those men, that it was contrary to hygiene and that everybody caught would have his name put in the paper. Thereupon they all of them produced their passports—we are accustomed to carry them about with us—"

" Is it so that you can go off to another country," I asked, " at a moment's notice ? "

He waved his forefinger from side to side. " It happens," he corrected me, " that one suddenly ceases to live—anywhere, in the street or somewhere else, with no one knowing who you are—and then it is useful if your passport is in your pocket."

" Even without the proper visa," said I.

" What do you mean ? " quoth the Serb. " Well,

there under the trees of the Café Balkan, they held out
their passports and the young woman took down their
names and they appeared in print without having to
pay a single dinar. Some people have the luck . . .
and that reminds me," he said, " that you are lucky.
I have heard just now of a gypsy—he plays in the band
at the other hotel—he has been sent away and, if you
like, he will walk with you across Slovakia. I have
told him to come here after you have had your lunch.
His name is Jozef Tokár."

Before I sat down to lunch in the fine dining-room
of the Hotel Slovan I went up to my own room and
rang for a maid, as I had to send some linen to the wash.
This maid turned out to be a stocky, middle-aged
woman. She threw the bundle of linen over her shoulder—I had enveloped all the articles in the pyjama
trousers—and she held the bundle in position by the
strings of the pyjamas. Then—one, two, one, two—
her solid, little body all erect, she marched like a gay
soldier down the corridor. But she had not gone more
than half-a-dozen yards when it seemed good to her
to be more feminine. So she came back to me and said
that she would have the linen ready by the time of my
return. And I, for my part, she suggested, might
reward her with a box of chocolates.

I would have rejoiced to take this little woman as
my comrade—of the gypsy I knew nothing save that
he had been dismissed—whereas this woman would
have been good company indeed.

She said that it would have been pleasant to go with me. She believed we would have been firm friends. It was unfortunate.

" But if the Serb will let you come with me," I said.

. . .

" We do not live in the Hungarian times when no one went to school unless he wanted to. And what was the use of it ? " she asked. " I myself went to a school where the instruction—I was very young—was all in the Hungarian language, and as I did not know that language, I learned as much arithmetic and reading as if I had been a parrot. But now we Slovaks go to Slovak schools and my son has to go. Otherwise—if you really mean it that I should travel with you—he might have walked with us. But if you and I set out there would be no one to look after him. I want him to become an educated man and then a lawyer."

I remarked that Slovakia seemed to be full of lawyers. Someone had told me that Banska Bystrica, for ex-ample, a place of a few thousand inhabitants, con-tained no less than thirty-three.

" It is the best thing," she said, " for a Slovak, because the people do no business without going to a lawyer."

" If they increase and increase," I objected, " then finally everyone will be a lawyer, and will one lawyer go for advice to another ? "

Her energetic face was clouded over for a moment. " Anyhow," she said. " My boy must not be truant from his school and you must go down for your lunch or there will be none left at all."

Well, there was still something left to eat, but for a time I did not overmuch enjoy it, since the Serb had evidently settled that the gypsy was to be my comrade. I had seen at the museum two small implements, most delicately wrought of wire. One had a loop that tightened round the leg of any hen which was attracted by the grain you sprinkled on the ground, the other implement consisted of a hook and a lassoo—the gypsies, I was told, were very skilful in that region— they were wont to wait until the peasants, men and women, had gone out into the fields, and then it did not take them long to drag a mattress through the window of a house. Jozef had perhaps been sent about his business on account of some such guilty conduct . . . yet even if he was a gatherer of hens and mattresses he might be a companionable fellow. And from me he certainly would be unable to acquire these two commodities. Thus I became more reconciled to having Jozef with me in my walk through Slovakia. Of course if he were to be lynched by furious peasants or else dragged before a magistrate, my walk would suffer permanent or temporary interruption.

At this moment Jozef came into the dining-room. He was a slender person, olive-skinned, and with a smile so frank and yet so full of mystery that I was fascinated.

He moved towards me.

I was on my feet. " Jozef," I began, " the proprietor has told me you would like to come to Orava."

He looked a little doubtful. " Yes, that is what he told me also," he agreed ; " but as I never once have been there in my life, I shall not be of service to you. I am sorry—I have always wished to see that castle. It has such a name."

" And," I said, " you shall see it."

" If you feel as I do," said Jozef, " a name like that sings through one's body."

What had I done, I asked myself, to have the reward of meeting such a man ?

" In your own country," I said, " there is an example of——"

" But alas ! we have no country."

" I beg your pardon. I should have said in Czecho-slovakia. Did you hear of that word, ' defenestration ', the punishment they thought appropriate for traitors ? What can be more agreeable than such a word ? "

He nodded gravely. " Yes, I like it very much," he said.

" Of course one cannot use it often," I remarked. " I mean the word. But how useful it is, altogether apart from the quality for which you and I admire it. For example, if you declare to a burglar that you intend to defenestrate him there and then, will he not—except if he is an abnormal burglar—be nonplussed and hesitate, thus putting opportunity into your hands ? Sup-posing also that you have to send a telegram about a person who has been flung out of a window this good word will be a saving of expense."

Before I had concluded these observations I had been aware that Jozef wished to speak, but that his courtesy prevented him from doing so. To this I made acknowledgment by the expression of my face.

" All that concerning the appropriate punishment," he said, " it interests me, I assure you. I have been dismissed because——"

There was a touch upon my elbow. " If you will not eat," the waiter said, " then it will all be cold."

" Stop ! " I cried to Jozef who was moving away.

" But you are not a gipsy," he said with a little, rueful smile as he turned his head for a moment. "We have a great advantage over you. When a horse dies of some illness and a chemical is poured over it and then it is buried, my people go to the place perhaps a week later in the night when there is no gendarme at the spot and they dig up the horse and scrape off the chemical and cook the beast and never do they suffer any inconvenience."

We had been gradually making for the door and when he turned his back on me I felt the hand of the solicitous young waiter once again upon my elbow. There was nothing left for me to do but to go back with him.

CHAPTER II

A VERY friendly interest was taken in our journey. From Turčiansky Svaty Martin to the castle of Orava is not so far as all that ; Jozef and I would have set out with no particular preparation, but this the public would not allow. We pointed out to them that I with my knapsack and Jozef with his impedimenta in a scarlet handkerchief were well equipped both for the days and for the nights. Moreover it would probably not occupy us beyond a couple of days, even if we loitered a good deal.

The prefect of the town, a very patriotic, middle-aged official—and one who, I imagine, would feel uneasy, not to say awkward if anyone should behold him without his respectable black suit and very sombre tie—this official was extremely anxious. He was good enough to come in person to the hotel and to announce to us that the success of our enterprise lay very near to his heart. If anything should happen to us on the way he would never forgive himself.

" You are too kind," I said, " but it would not be your fault."

" As for me," said Jozef cheerfully, " I have wandered here and there, and up to now I have not suffered much."

23

" Now listen to me," begged the prefect. " What I have to propose is this : would it not be better if you went by train ? Oh yes, I know that you have resolved to walk. But very often in life it is a very good thing if one changes one's mind. I believe that the man who never changes his mind has not got a mind to change." He glanced at Jozef and at me and it was clear that he was most uncomfortable. Then suddenly he had a new idea—he produced some money and asked Jozef if he would go to a certain little shop—he described where it was—for some salami.

" But really," I protested, " why should you——"

The prefect interrupted me. " If nothing," he said, " will make you turn back from your travels, then at any rate I must be permitted to make a small contribution. It would hurt me very much if you decline."

No sooner had Jozef left the room—we were in my bedroom—than the prefect's manner underwent a rapid change. His face assumed an awful solemnity and there he stood in the middle of the room, confronting me, like some early Father of the Church, with uplifted forefinger.

I began to feel uneasy and I told him so.

" But that is nothing to what you might feel," he declared, " if you do not take with you the salami."

" Oh, but there is sure to be a hostelry between here and Orava," I said. " There is no fear that we would starve."

The prefect gazed at me with very penetrating eyes

and when he spoke the words came forth impressively. "You have not heard perhaps about our cannibals? No, you have not, I see. Down in the south-east of Slovakia is a village. But the natives of it are in prison, for they have confessed to being cannibals."

I was astounded. "Do you mean," I said, "that here in Czechoslovakia which is the most orderly State of Central Europe, in Czechoslovakia with its— its stabilized currency and——"

"I mean," he said, "that we have cannibals. It is true that they are only gipsies and it is also true that the police do not believe them, because they say that the gipsies are like children who want to be the centre of interest and that they are only saying this with that object. On the other hand it may be true. And what if your Jozef should be a cannibal? That is why I request you to take the salami. It may save your life."

"You think he will prefer the salami?"

The shadow of a smile passed over his solemn face. "Forgive me if I say so," he said, "but I think nearly everyone would prefer the salami."

He was now somewhat relieved. I would not be entirely without armour. But several other points, he told me, had to be discussed. Ere we could do so, however, we received the visit of the sturdy maid who had marched off with my soiled linen. In accordance with her usual practice she refrained from knocking at the door. And this time, at any rate, that child of nature caused me less embarrassment than on one or two other occasions.

Apparently she did not know that the black-coated gentleman was her prefect; but she was the essence of courtesy.

"Sir," she said to him, "if you are giving advice before he goes I likewise want to give him some. But I will wait."

"Well," said the prefect, "it is kind of you. I thought I would inquire if he is in good training for a walk." And he turned to me.

"I want to ask about his boots," said the maid, "they are the most important things when you are walking. I have got a brother-in-law who is at Bata's and they are really very good boots."

"I daresay," said the prefect, "but would you mind if I ask him whether he is in training?"

"That story," I said, "about the famous chess-player who, when he was asked the same question, announced that he did not go in for any special training, except to take a bath some days before the beginning of a tournament, I know that story. And I think I can be just as confident as he was."

"I am glad to hear it," said the prefect.

Meanwhile the maid had seated herself upon the bed; her hands were folded; it was evident that she proposed to stay there for some time.

She saw that I was looking at her and forthwith she started: "Bata's factory," she said, "is . . ."

" Oh," said the prefect, " if you are going to talk of Bafa's you are not the only one who is interested in that." And he sat down on the greenish divan which was at the other side of the apartment.

It would have been inconvenient for me to stand there in the middle of the room, now bending this way and now that. So I sat down beside the maid.

" My brother-in-law a few years ago," quoth she, " was nothing, what you would call a little man. And now with the greatest ease he nourishes his family and has a motor-car. God knows what he will have next. He works at Bafa's."

" I have been to Zlin," said the prefect. " Of course everyone is not interested in the manufacture of boots, but I hope we are all interested in the making of men. It is really a remarkable place."

" True, true, very true," exclaimed the maid, and in order to add some further emphasis she struck me on the knee, an act of which she evidently was un-conscious. " Would you believe it that when my brother-in-law—some people are born like that, to be lucky—when he married he received a house of four rooms with central heating and a white enamel bath and a garden, all that for nineteen crowns a week."

" In your money," said the prefect to me, " that is less than two shillings and sixpence. As I was saying just now, it is the making of the next generation that I, when I was at Zlin, paid most attention to. Between the ages of fourteen and seventeen the boys have gratuitous lessons for three hours every evening. I believe that English, German and some other subjects are going to be made obligatory. Baťa believes in English. I saw an inscription outside the library, that it breaks a window into the world. By the way those inscriptions of his are painted in huge black letters on the white wall that runs round the whole place. ' Our customer is our master,' says one. ' After good work let us have good play,' says another. One, at the entrance to a workshop, was to the effect that if you didn't clean your boots at home you should also refrain from doing it there—and thus you would feel more homely. But I was telling you about the boys. They earn 300 or 400 crowns a week— it depends on their industry—and what do they have to pay ? Their bed in the dormitory costs them four crowns a week, a breakfast with a couple of eggs costs them two crowns and the chief meal of the day—soup, meat, vegetables and a sweet—either three or four crowns. So they can save a good deal and Baťa gives them ten per cent on their savings. The boys are put onto a different job every three months, in order to find out the one which is most congenial to them. Dear me, I have been making quite a speech."

" What does he do with the boys," I asked, " who are not on piece-work ? "

" You mean the engineers and the clerks and those who test the leather and—well, they receive good pay. For instance I heard of a clerk who is sixteen

years old and he gets 240 crowns a week and Bata
is so pleased with him that he gives him a present of
10,000 crowns each Christmas. Of course Bata looks
after his people's health—all kinds of games are encouraged—and he urges them to eat fruit. Some years
ago an orange at Zlin was sold for eight crowns. He
advised the dealers to sell them for one crown, which
would tremendously increase their trade. ' Impossible,' they answered. So he sent one of his young
men to Italy and told him that he must bring back
oranges to sell for half a crown. The young man
returned with three railway vans of oranges—he spent
his days and nights among them, to be sure that they
would arrive safely. In fact," said the prefect, " it
would not strike you, perhaps, that Bata's people are
slaves ? "

" That they are slaves ? " I asked.

" Well, there was a book written by a German who
made this accusation. Germany is suffering a great
deal from the competition of Bata. I heard the other
day, as it happens, that in Pirmasens, which is, I
believe, the most important boot-manufacturing centre
in Germany, at Pirmasens large numbers of the em-
ployees in the boot factories wear Bata's boots ! "

The maid had been for some little time eager to get
in a word. The bed, which on the previous night I
had found quite stable enough for its allotted purpose,
was palpitating under her excitement.

" My brother-in-law has told me," she said, " that

the people in the factory have to buy their boots like everyone else. Outside the gate there is a boot shop and as the workers come out they stare in at the window just like the ordinary public."

At that moment my friend Jozef returned to us with a long piece of salami wrapped up in a strip of white paper. I motioned to him to sit down and he did so, without uttering a word, by the side of the prefect.

" That reminds me," said the prefect, " of the food at Bata's."

" Excuse me," I said, " but you have alluded to it."

" It is so good in the canteen that when Mrs. Bata has an afternoon party she buys her cakes there. But, after all, the chief thing about a boot factory is boots. Ten to twelve thousand calf and other skins are needed every day—many of them are from South America. Bata gets them from there, makes them into boots, sends the boots to North America and beats the Yankees by one dollar. He is continually trying to introduce improvements—if he can save a fraction of a crown or of a minute he will throw away the old machinery and put in something else. They used to cut the loose threads with a knife ; he found that it saved a second or two if the ends were burned off, and so he provided hundreds of little flames. Did I tell you that he has various newspapers ? One of them is edited by Bert Ženatý, a well-known Slovak writer who has lived in America. There is a paper for the children and a humorous paper, and if any of them have more than a

certain weekly sale the surplus is shared among the
people on that paper, from the editorial staff down to
the paper boys. It is like that in the factory—if one
of the workshops turns out more than 2,000 pairs in a
day there is a bonus for everyone."

"Everything at Bața's seems to be," I said, "for
the best."

"But they place obstacles in his path," said the prefect. "I went over that splendid school he has built.
Between the top of the heating apparatus and the
windows he left a ledge on which he wanted each of the
pupils to have a little plant in a pot. For more than
one reason it would have been a very good thing ; but
the school-inspector said there was no precedent. He
therefore vetoed it and a casing was added, to be flush
with the windows—of course at Bața's expense—so
that there should be no room for the plants."

"I would like to go there someday," I said.

"My brother-in-law," began the maid, " . . ."

"When I went," said the prefect, "it was with Bert
Ženatý. The great advantage of going anywhere with
an observant man is that he will point out the little
things that are tremendous. As we walked into a workshop there was Bața himself—and he, the multi-
millionaire, the biggest boot-manufacturer in the world,
was at a sewing-machine, explaining to four men and
two women some new fashion for dealing with a couple
of pieces of leather. He got up to greet us, he preceived
that we were in the excellent hands of Ženatý and then

he sat down again to his demonstration with enthusiasm written all over him. He is a psychologist also—he lets the girls dress themselves as they please, but he is glad if they abandon the national costume and take to short skirts and short hair. He says that a girl in the traditional costume is less wide-awake than the modern girl. Oh yes, Bata is a psychologist. He used to have 150 accountants who put down the daily earnings of the hands; now the people put these down themselves on a large sheet that is near the door of each workshop; and so now there is no dispute and it is impossible for anyone to put down too much, as each person is controlled by his neighbours. It is no exaggeration to say that Bata is paternal. When the price of sugar looked, not long ago, as if it would be seriously raised, he forthwith bought a sugar-factory. He was not going to have his people imposed upon. And the general public may, if they like, avail themselves of his stores. The amount of soap that is now used all around Zlin is unprecedented, for he sells it, like everything else, at a very low price. The health of the whole district has greatly improved. For those who are threatened with tuberculosis he has several sanatoria where they go to recuperate and the hospital, the only thing of which he has given the supervision to someone else, an eminent doctor, cost him eight million crowns. By the way he finds employment for about a hundred blind people who, for the most part, make boxes. It is a pathetic sight to see them in the canteen, with a normal person here and there among them who cuts up their meat."

I have no doubt but that the prefect and the maid could have continued their doxology for a week. I told them that henceforward I would contemplate my boots with such an interest as I had never felt.

Soon after this the pair of them left me and I was alone with Jozef.

It appeared to me that he had a defiant air. I asked him if he was by chance an anti-Baťa man.

He shook his head as he got up and stalked off to the window.

But before I could as much as wonder what was in his mind he turned and faced me. " I am going to tell you," he said " what was the cause of my dismissal. But you will not send me away ? I want to go with you."

" And I want to take you." I said, " and I *will* take you."

The door was opened. There stood the prefect. " Pardon me, but I forgot," he said, " about those five hundred women in New York."

" And do you think that they would pardon you ? "

" Their feet are not like those of European women and so Baťa got their measurements. He does the same for every country in the world. If the Republic of Hayti were to command all its citizens to wear boots, then Baťa would be able to supply them in a few days with exactly the proper models. When a new model has to be executed he thinks nothing of working all night and his special staff is delighted to do so—meals are sent to them at intervals and couches placed at their disposal for a little rest. They are so enthusiastic that they would throw themselves into this extra work even if there were no extra pay. I can remember when Bata—he used to have one assistant and now he employs about 13,000 and he is a man in the prime of life—I can remember when he was scoffed at, because he wanted to introduce American methods. They pointed out to him that the natives of Zlin and the neighbourhood are not Americans and that one cannot change a human being. But the people of that part of our country, at all events 13,000 of them, are quite different from what they would have been if no Bata had appeared. They seem to be as wide-awake as Bata himself and often they make, as they are invited to do, suggestions for rendering the factory more efficient ; of course any suggestion that is accepted is paid for, besides which the person who makes it is in future a marked man, marked out for promotion."

Thereupon the prefect disappeared again and Jozef was telling me that in the course of an evening performance he had burst into song, while at the same time he continued to play on his violin and to conduct the band. They had been playing very well, but for one reason or another the diners ate and ate, as if the music had not been there. Then Jozef sang a song of hatred. He was using his own language. But there came a great misfortune—in the room was someone who could understand the Romany. What did that person do but go to the proprietor of the hotel—it was not so much to denounce poor Jozef as to display his erudition. And the result was that the owner of the place threw Jozef out.

So we arranged that we would leave on the next morning.

CHAPTER III

BEFORE Jozef appeared in my room with his violin-case in one hand, in the other his scarlet handkerchief that encircled the rest of his luggage I had been entertaining the proprietor of the hotel and the sturdy, little maid. Perhaps entertaining is not the right word, because each of them when they arrived, first the maid and then, after about a quarter of an hour, the Serb expressly said that they did not intend to trouble me and that I was to make my toilette just as if they were not present.

It would have been ungracious of me if I had evinced any stage-fright in front of my small audience—she sat herself down very soberly on the divan—but even if I had been one of those greatly honoured actresses of our time who show the public in every play how they disrobe and go to bed—for the public is sound enough and always anxious to watch an expert—even if I had been such a lady I am not sure whether the minuteness of my audience would not have embarrassed me.

I did not quite gather why the maid was there at all. If she had come to offer me advice she kept it to herself ; her aspect was not cheerful. So too when the Serb arrived he added nothing to the gaiety of

36

nations. Side by side these two untoward visitors of mine sat there and looked at me, as if I was about to be conducted to my execution.

In the street, a herd of cows, with bells attached to them, were passing by, for Turčiansky is a rural little town. But this gay music did not alter anything in the sad faces that regarded me.

"Well then," I said, as I thrust in the tail of my shirt, "suppose we talk of executioners. You really remind me of Ellis, the hare-lipped executioner of England."

"I have never been to England," said the maid.

"It was always his custom," I said, "to examine his clients on the day before he had to deal with them. But he did it in a pleasant, unobtrusive way, through a tiny hole in the door of the condemned cell. And when he had estimated their weight he filled a sack with . . . I don't know what he put into the sack."

"And nevertheless," said the Serb, "you know a lot about this man. But England"—he heaved a sigh—"is a great country. Look at the size of your newspapers."

Then, as I buttoned on my braces, I told him and the maid how Ellis would make experiments with the sack, in order to ascertain how much drop he should allow. And he was never the same man, I told them, after the hanging of Mrs. Thompson, the Ilford murderess. His estimate had been as correct as usual, but on the next morning she was in such a state of collapse that she had to be carried out and hanged in a chair, and this upset all Ellis's calculations.

Neither the melancholy Serb nor yet the maid gave any outward sign of exhilaration.

" It is very good of you," I said to the proprietor, " that you are taking my journey so to heart. I do wish, though, that you could bring yourself to look on the bright side of things. I assure you there is always a happy side, if only . . ."

" If only," he interrupted, " one knew which it were. Have you heard of Mestrovitch, our great sculptor, the greatest sculptor, I suppose, in the world ? I have had the news from Belgrade that his monument has been erected in the park. It is a monument of Victory, a nude heroic figure of a man, which ought to have been placed on the Terazia, as we call it, the central point of Belgrade, high above the railway-station and the river, with a marvellous view of that green, endless plain which we secured by the war. But the authorities could not determine whether the Victory should confront the people who drive up into the town or whether he should turn to them his other side."

" To receive them in that fashion," I said, " would be unusual."

" The citizens wanted to learn by the example of New York, where the statue of Liberty looks away from the town. And so our Belgrade statue was not to have that reproach. Some of the municipal authorities did not like it whether it were to face the north or the south, because it has no clothing. So what they have done is to plant it in the park Kalemegdan, where one need not see it every day unless one goes there on purpose. And it will be clothed a little by the shadows of the trees."

" Are you mourning," I asked, " on account of your people's appreciation of a great artist ? "

" At any rate," said the Serb, as he thrust his gloom away from him, " at any rate the park is in Belgrade too and thus the town has a fine piece of sculpture, which is more than one can say for many other towns which are more prominent than Belgrade."

I was glad to see that he was now in quite a good humour. How could I produce this consummation in the maid ? Another monument, perhaps—it occurred to me that I might tell her about one at Olomouc, the seat of an archbishop, which is not so very distant, as the crow flies, from Turčiansky. Also it was the only other monument of which I knew the slightest tale. But as I ran the brushes through my hair I recognized that she would be left very cold by Julius Cæsar. It would be much better for me to refrain from telling how the place was once called Olomunz or Olomons and then had asked itself if this did not derive from Oliomons, Joliomons, Julii mons, and if so, who was Julius ? Some Roman coins were discovered in a neighbouring hill and the eighteenth-century people of Olomouc were persuaded that their town had been founded by Julius Cæsar. If you had told them that he never crossed the Danube they would have replied that it was the easiest thing for him to be represented at the ceremony. But all this and the fact that the emperor is portrayed upon a prancing steed, nonchalantly riding it with no bridle and no stirrup, all this would have made no particular appeal to the maid Maria and for that reason I did not refer to it.

I began to feel—and perhaps not I alone—that our journey was a long time in getting under way. And yet, as I looked at the Serbian proprietor and his dour, little Slovak maid it occurred to me that if I remained at Turčiansky I would, with their assistance, discover a great deal about Slovakia and maybe more than some travellers have been able to find after having put themselves to the inconvenience of rushing up and down the country. For example, in a recent book by a London journalist, the details came for the most part, according to the author's statement, from non-official persons living in Slovakia. I had been surprised at some of the remarks and, as the writer had not verified them, I determined to do so on his behalf.

I sat down on the bed and told my visitors that an Englishman had been writing a book with a number of odd things in it, a book about Slovakia.

" I am very pleased to hear it," said the Serb, " and

I hope it will be translated. We younger nations have very few books to make us laugh."

" Whether it was written for that purpose," I said, " I am not sure. Yet he puts in one place that the railway guards are not allowed to answer anyone in German, although they may write an answer in that language."

" Oh, but what a man he is ! " cried the maid, as she leaned back and burst into a roar of laughter, while with her dangling legs she made convulsive movements. " Think of it," she exclaimed, " the guard, like a deaf and dumb fellow, taking out a pencil and a piece of paper."

I mentioned another passage from the same book in which the writer spoke of Jachymov, the place where radium is obtained. That is the Slav name of the ancient village. Before the war it was generally known by its German name, Joachimsthal. The silver mines in the vicinity were used for the coins called joachimsthalers, afterwards abbreviated into thalers, and the word dollar has the same deriviation. Our author objects to the Slav form Jachymov on the ground that : " no philologist will be able to trace the ancestry of the word dollar to Jachymov " . . . " Have you ever heard," I said, " a more delicious and more truthful sentence ? "

The Serb was in a very happy mood. " I thank you for telling me about that book," he said. " Here in Turčiansky I sometimes find it monotonous, the

long winter evenings ; but now it will all be changed.
I will enjoy myself with the book of that man. Tell
me another of his funny notions, I entreat you. Did
he get them all out of his own head, do you think ? "

At that moment the door opened and Jozef came in,
with his violin-case and the bulging scarlet handkerchief.

" If you please," said the Serb, " do not take him
away for a little time. We are in the middle of a very
good conversation."

Jozef was quite ready to fall in with this request.
As he went over to the window, on whose ledge he
perched himself, he said that we were going to have a
fine and windy day.

" That is so," said the Serb, " and if you were in a
hurry I think I would walk with you for a part of the
way, as our friend is amusing me so much. And do
you suppose," he asked of me, " that the man got all
of that out of his own head ? "

" From internal evidence," I answered, " it seems
to me that he got a good deal from Hungarians. I
don't believe that he wishes to show his contempt for
this country by refusing to call the towns by their
names on the map, but by preferring the Hungarian
names. He simply wrote down, I imagine, in the most
blissful ignorance, the names as they fell from the lips
of his informants."

" If," said the Serb in a judicial kind of voice, " if I
were going to write a book I think I would go to the

different people in a country, and as there are Hungarians enough in Slovakia, in the South of Slovakia, your man did what was right. Yes, there are Hungarians enough. A gentleman who comes here sometimes from Bratislava, Dr. Štefánek, the deputy*— he told me that 35,000 Hungarians at the last election were so satisfied with everything that they would not vote for the Hungarian deputies who oppose the Government, but for the Agrarian Party, which is in the Government. Well, I hope your man consulted some of those Hungarians who are content."

" Why should they not be content," put in the maid, " when they have—the gentleman who looks after the schools told me so himself the last time he was here—when such and such a number of them have more Hungarian schools in our country than in Hungary! That is the way we treat them—and what did they do ? What kind of a school did they have for me when I was a Slovak child ? I tell you the lessons were in Hungarian."

" Do you mean to say . . ."

" Oh, yes, some of the elementary schools were Slovak, but not the one in my village or in many other villages. For the last twenty, thirty years of their rule the Hungarians did everything possible to wipe out the Slovak people, as if the Slovaks were not as good as themselves."

" Just so ! " exclaimed the Serb. " What have they

*Subsequently Minister of Education.

done in literature or in music or in anything else that we Slavs have not done quite as well ? "

" What I want to tell you is this," said the maid. She was sitting bolt upright, her face was drawn. " A newspaper in Budapest," she said, " the *Pesti Hirlap*, gave a big prize every year to a schoolmaster in the region of Hungary that was not inhabited by Hungarians if that schoolmaster could make all the people or most of them talk Hungarian. The village of Deven in Slovakia got it one year, I mean the schoolmistress got it. Her name was Feher."

" But," I said, " how well you are informed ! "

" I take an interest in things," she answered, " and the prize was a thousand florins."

The proprietor of the hotel was laughing to himself. " It is curious," he said, " that you should speak about the *Pesti Hirlap*, because I heard a nice thing of it just the other day. Several customers of mine were talking of how the elections were conducted in the old days. A gentleman called Legrady, the owner of the *Pesti Hirlap*, was a candidate somewhere. It was at his office that the taxation booklets were printed, and so the rival candidate told the electors that it was Legrady who taxed them—there was his name at the end of the book, for anyone to read—and as a matter of fact this caused Legrady to lose the election. . . . We are keeping you too long," he said, " but there is one thing more about that book you spoke of. We have some problems in Slovakia that are serious, though they are being gradually solved. Yet they are serious and I would like to know if he has managed to be funny about them. What does he say, for example, about Agrarian Reform ? I know something about that," said the proprietor, " as the people who come here like to talk of it. They have been talking of it for years."

So far as I remembered the author of the book did not get hold of anything humorous to say about the land settlement. Perhaps he did not have such opportunities as if he had been describing the settlement of the frontiers in Central and South-Eastern Europe. He would, maybe, have told us in that case of a person on the Yugoslav-Roumanian boundary in the Banat who has the frontier running through his house, so that the lavatory is in Roumania, and if this householder were a law-abiding citizen he would never go to that part of his house except if a visa had been placed on his passport. It would take about two or three weeks for a passport to go to Bucharest and return with the visa. The author might have alluded to the ridiculous situation at another part of the same frontier where the railway from Bazias on the Danube belongs to Roumania for a mile or two and then enters Yugoslavia, while a couple of Yugoslav villages have also been given to Roumania for a reason that no man has yet fathomed. The inhabitants could walk to Bela Crkva, a fairly large town, in half an hour, but as it is they have to go to market thirty miles away across a range of mountains ; and, some time ago, when there was a fire in one of these villages, the fire-brigade had to come from Bela Crkva, that is to say from another country, to put it out.

"With regard to land settlement," I said, "it has been alleged that the Hungarian landowners in Czechoslovakia have been outrageously treated, because they have been given such a very low compensation for their land, for the land they may no longer possess now that nobody may have more than a certain amount."

"Yes, but wait a minute," cried the Serb. "Practically all the landowners were in debt to their banks and they have had to pay them on the same scale as their own compensation. Do you understand ? It was arranged that an Austro-Hungarian pre-war crown should be represented by six post-war Czechoslovak crowns. Of course a landowner can, if he likes, call down the vengeance of Heaven because he is being paid 1,000 crowns instead of 6,000 ; but he does not usually mention that instead of paying his bank 6,000 he only has to pay 1,000."

"To return to the allegations," I said, "I will do my best to remember one or two examples. Thus there is the estate of a man called Gustavus Láng near the village of Karva, of which seventy-five joch* were allotted to the peasants. A complaint was made

*A joch in pre-war Hungary and in the present Slovakia is about an acre.

that it was difficult for the Hungarian peasant to get any land."

" But I know about that place, I know it very well," said the Serb. " There are three other men, Julius Szöke, Kosticz and Szarvassy, who have all got larger properties than Gustavus Láng, and they have, each of them, been obliged to sell one hundred joch. The people of the neighbourhood used to earn their bread on the other side of the river in the cement works or the tile manufactory on else in the iron works a little further off. They had to do that because the land on their own side was all in the possession of those four persons. When the new frontier prevented them from going to work across the river a good many of them became Communists. And when it was proposed to let them have some land, that Mr. Szöke objected. ' They are Communists ! ' he said. ' But they are human beings ! ' he was answered. In short Mr. Szöke—and there are plenty of Hungarian land-owners who resemble him—did not want to do anything with regard to land for his own compatriots."

" How selfish of them," I remarked.

" But we must not misjudge them. They are patriotic too," said the Serb with a little laugh. " You see, Hungary is the most feudal country in Europe and if the Hungarian peasant in Czechoslovakia can get more land than the peasants on the other side of the Danube, they will listen less and less to any anti-Czech propaganda."

" But are they really receiving land in this country?" I asked.

" Why don't you believe it ? I can hear by your voice that you don't. Well, I happen to know that over thirty-six thousand hectares* have been allotted already to the Hungarian peasants. It is impossible to give everyone land who wants it. In the whole Republic I believe something like forty-two per cent of the applications have to be refused. And isn't it right that the Slovaks, who for centuries were treated as the State's step-children, should be granted, in proportion, more land than the Hungarians, whose position is so much better ? Yet there is no policy of revenge. . . . But you talked about selfish people a little time ago, and I shall be that if I keep you longer."

At these words my prospective fellow-traveller, Jozef, who was sitting on the window-ledge, arose and stretched himself. Then, after he had picked up his violin-case and his luggage in the scarlet handkerchief, he stalked out of the room. On his way he nodded at the pair upon the divan. Probably he thought that if he lingered we would start again discussing this and that.

I stood up and walked after him. And as I went I hitched my knapsack on.

" Go with God," exclaimed the Serb, as I touched his hand and that of the sturdy, little maid.

" Who knows where I shall sleep to-night ? " I said.

*A hectare is nearly 2½ acres.

" May you fall into good hands," said the Serb.
" An old gentleman came here the other evening—he
said that he might die—and I told him that he could
have a room, even if he was going to do that kind of
thing."

CHAPTER IV

THERE is nothing sensational about Turčiansky.
Though it has one of the oldest—and, incidentally, one
of the ugliest—churches in Slovakia, with several other
aged buildings, yet the average person, save in his
morbid moments, would not think that any of the
architecture deserves to be photographed. Nor does
Turčiansky occupy a dominating situation. If it did,
then there would be the trusty, mediaeval walls and the
proud gateways which we find in various other Slovak
towns. But there are no such things ; where
Turčiansky ends one looks in vain for picturesqueness.
After the last little house you step into the open
country.

It is a rather prosperous plain, encircled with
mountains ; and on the day when we travelled over
it our progress and our conversation were rendered
difficult by the wind. Whether that turbulent fellow
found his way through a cleft in the mountains or
whether he leaped exultingly over them, at all events
he charged across the plain as if his life depended on
it. His course and ours were not in direct opposition,
for he came at us obliquely, and what we had to do was
to lean against him. I was not yet on such intimate
terms with Jozef as to be able to be in his company

and speak no word. So, making a great effort, I bellowed at him that we were not men as trees walking, since a tree inclines in the same direction as the wind.

After we had struggled on for a few minutes Jozef shouted at me that he had just remembered the name of another kind of tree, the coconut palm. " It usually leans into the wind," cried Jozef, " even as you and I are doing."

It would have been pleasant to know why this particular tree behaves so perversely ; but, for all I knew, it would have entailed a long explanation which, under the circumstances, I wanted to spare both Jozef and myself.

" Another time," I roared at him, " another time we will talk about the coconut palm."

He eyed me gravely and nodded. As we continued our laborious advance the mountains, at which we now and then looked, did not seem to be appreciably nearer. And, if the wind should fail to moderate, our task in traversing those formidable mountains—on the presumption that the road went over them and not between them—would be almost an impossibility.

Now Jozef, being wiser, did not think of the prospective hardships. His meditations, in fact, were still occupied with the coconut palm.

" I wonder," he said, " where is the home of that tree, the one we are going to talk about."

I moved my hand in such a manner as to indicate a considerable distance.

4

" Well, I would like to go there," he said. " There is so much to be seen in this world."

" If there is a village," I said—and, shielding one of my eyes with the inside of a hand I gazed along the dreary, wind-swept road.

" Two leagues from this place—can you hear me ? " cried Jozef, " there is a village with a hostelry."

I also had been thinking of that hostelry. " When we are there," I said, " then you must tell me of your travels."

He laughed bitterly. " There is not much difference," he said, " between me and a certain old woman whom I heard of. A friend of mine landed on her island. It is in the Adriatic, a brief voyage from the larger island of Hvar, and it is one of the few places in south-eastern Europe where no minority exists. The population is content. Of course you have not heard of it."

" Did you say that the population consists of an old woman ? " I asked.

" It is a lovely little island , so my friend informed me, and the old woman lives with a multitude of wild asses. Perhaps they are the descendants of some ordinary domestic asses which have been allowed to return to a state of nature."

" But why did the old woman go to such a solitude ? "

" That," said Jozef, " is what I wanted to know. According to my friend, her aspect was by no means repulsive, and she displayed no evidence of any foul disease. On the other hand she had obviously not chosen to dwell in exile because of any devastating beauty which might set men by the ears. She was, in fact, a rather corpulent old lady, neither hideous nor the reverse, one whom in a crowd you would scarcely notice. ' I came here,' she told my friend, ' many years ago.' ' It would be very kind of you,' he said, ' if you will tell me your story.' ' But what is there to tell ? ' said she. ' I live here and I cultivate chrysan-themums. When the fishermen land here they sleep in my house. But the chrysanthemums produce more insect powder than I need ; and all the rest I send away with the fishermen. When they come back they give me the money.' ' That,' said my friend, ' is a good arrangement, but you might have cultivated them on a larger island. When you have no visits from the fishermen it must be very lonely for you. And the wild asses. . . .' ' I leave them alone and they leave me alone,' said the old lady. She looked out over the water and for some time there was no word spoken. Then : ' I will not ask you,' said my friend, ' why you came to this place. No doubt you had an excellent reason.' ' Well, well,' said she, ' who knows ? All that I remember is that I have been here many years.' "

While he had been telling me all this the wind had not abated. Clumps of grass beside the road and the grey, little pools of water on it—for this was an unfre-quented thoroughfare—were shuddering. But Jozef and myself were much less incommoded than we had

been. He could talk and I could listen with com-
parative facility. So I was meditating on the noble
nature of man ; unconsciously I spoke my thoughts
aloud.

" What are you saying about other animals ? " asked
Jozef.

" At any rate," I said, " we are nobler than the
vegetables, because we can adapt ourselves. Look
at the grass."

" Excuse me," said Jozef, " but there are many
people in Central Europe who believe that a vegetable
is much nobler than a gipsy. They would be astonished that you should agree to walk with one of us.
Perhaps there is a little improvement now, but I have
seen, yes I have seen with my own eyes, when this
land was under the Hungarians, I have seen them in a
café spitting on a piece of paper money and then
calling up the gipsy musician and plastering it on his
forehead. But you were asking me to look at the
grass."

I had wanted to say that it was suffering as much as
ever and that we, on the other hand, were adaptable
and that I never felt more glad that I was human.
How could I say this, however, when poor Jozef and
his folk were treated as if they were not human beings ?

" Why do you want me to look at the grass ? "

I said that I was glad to hear that his people were
receiving better treatment. Then they likewise would
be glad that they had been created human beings.

" Yes, yes," quoth Jozef, " but it has its inconvenience. For example, I am very hungry. I
suppose i⁺ is the wind."

" That," I said, " is why we brought the salami."
Of course I remembered what the prefect had told
me about the anthropophagous gipsies.

" It is odd, but I do not like salami," said Jozef.

We were a long way from the nearest house and if
I had screamed for assistance it would have been as
useful as an anchor in the middle of the ocean. But
to associate Jozef with cannibalism was ridiculous.
And it was ridiculous of the prefect to recommend the
salami, which I could offer instead of myself. What
a good thing, though, that Jozef was the man he
was. It would have been most awkward if he had
been different, if he had been addicted to human
flesh, since in his case the salami would have been of
no avail. There, on the unpopulated plain, I would
have cut a sorry figure, for I—hoping against hope—
would have done my best to speak badly of myself
and, on the other hand, to exalt the salami. It is
well to be modest, but there are limits ; and when it
comes to singing the praise of a sausage and depre-
cating yourself, I think one is a traitor to one's
kind.

" If you do not care for salami," I said, " then
there is nothing for you to eat. I am very sorry."

" It is my own fault," said Jozef.

As we plodded on the wind became more boisterous

than ever, with occasional sharp gusts of rain. The violin-case knocked continually against Jozef's leg.

Hitherto we had derived some solace from the thought that we were approaching a village where there was a hostelry and that, once inside its walls, we would contemplate with satisfaction this disagreeable part of the journey. It has been said that there is nothing we endure more easily than the misfortunes of other people ; but what is so delicious as to look back on the perils that we have survived ? They, at all events, do not grow dim with the advancing years ; in fact they grow.

Well, we had soothed ourselves by thinking of that hostelry. But in the more and more disastrous weather we became morose. I had not as yet seen Jozef look so grim, and when the violin-case struck his leg again, not very violently, he astonished me by his extreme exasperation.

" No, no," I could hear him muttering to himself.

A pool of water on the road obliged me for a little to walk just behind him. He was marching in a way that showed his iron resolution. He had certainly made up his mind—and that he did not intend to be diverted was quite obvious.

What was it ? Evidently something which demanded a considerable effort. This was even more palpable when we once again were walking side by side—he pressed his lips together, but he wore at the same time a look of pathos, as if he was burdened with too great

a task. It must be something of no common mag-
nitude. Suppose it was the direst of ordeals, that he
was endeavouring to smother his ancestral passions.

Was he, after all, a man-eater and was he doing
his utmost to forgo me? How long would he be
capable of holding out? It was indeed a situation.

Then I told myself it was absurd to think that such
a charming, sympathetic fellow could have such un-
sociable habits. But I knew so little about anthropophagous persons and thus to accuse them roundly of
being deficient in charm and sympathy would be most
unwarranted, not to say dangerous. It would cause
me, when in the society of the charming and the
sympathetic, to be off my guard with respect to their
latent man-eating proclivities. And there and then
I vowed that, if haply I should survive this walk
with Jozef, no external polish in a person would ever
again lull me into feeling quite secure.

Jozef's teeth pressed on his under-lip. There was a
stern rigidity about the lines of his face and this was
emphasised by the way in which the rim of his brown
hat was moving to and fro, while some strands of
his long hair flew likewise in the wind.

I had been so preoccupied with what Jozef might do
that I had given not a thought to any action I myself
could undertake. But why should not I, as the expression is, sell my life dearly? Why should I sell
it at all?

Maybe that the struggle would be sharp and short.

One could very well imagine that a meritorious cannibal, perceiving that the other person did not share his views, would wash his hands of the whole business. Possibly as a connoisseur of human flesh, he would know that such flesh as resisted would lose a good deal of its suavity. Or he might, not thinking of his dinner, be repelled by someone of such different ideas. If I resisted I might not have to fight very long.

And then, perhaps, we would soon be friends again. For my part I hoped that I was not so unintelligent as to demand that everyone should look on life as I did. And he, if I had not misjudged him, would be equally prepared to associate with someone in the opposite camp. What a horrible world it would be if our private opinions were universal.

I was anxious to retain my fellow-traveller's friendship. He appeared to me to be just the sort of man with whom it is pleasant to go on a journey. I resolved that in maintaining my own point of view on this particular question I would refrain from doing so in a brutal way that would hurt his feelings. I would defend myself strenuously and, I hoped, successfully ; but I would not forget to be courteous.

Then, as I glanced at him—we were again walking side by side—it became apparent that Jozef was engaged in a terrific battle with himself. His mouth was twitching and he dug his nails convulsively into the palm of his hand. Yet that which made on me the

profoundest impression was when—not looking towards me, but gazing ahead—he tightened his belt.
Was this the final effort he was making to overcome
his ravenous hunger ?

Should I leap upon him and derive the advantage
of getting in the first blow ? Or should I, with greater
courage, do nothing and await his attack ? Yes, let
me be courageous. Let me have the supreme fortitude
of Don Fulano, that celebrated matador in white
who used to stand on a small box in the middle of the
arena and, without flinching, await the onslaught. I
had heard of his achievements long ago, but I had a
vague, uneasy feeling that at last a bull had called his
bluff.

It was with a feeling of heroism, a tremendous but
elated sentiment, that I travelled onward. And
when we came to the village street, which mostly
consisted of pale-blue or white-washed walls, with at
intervals a little house that was at right angles to the
street, and when we stepped into the hostelry, whose
metal sign was creaking in the wind, I felt a trifle sad
to be reduced to ordinary life and that my great ad-
venture was concluded. I had surely qualified myself
to be the protagonist of a glorious boy's book. Now
my hour of heroism was at an end, but for the rest of
my days I would remember how I had passed along
a grievous road, exhibiting no sign of perturbation,
although in the presence of a danger one is rarely
called upon to meet.

There was no hall or passage in that hostelry ; the street door opened onto the guest-room, a sombre apartment with a table going round two sides of it and a wooden bench between the table and the dirty wall. Several villagers were sitting behind glasses of beer and the landlord, a tall, grave man, was standing in the centre of the room and talking to them. From his attitude and theirs it seemed as if they were discussing matters they regarded as ephemeral. Most of the customers lounged on the benches as if they were sumptuous sofas, while the landlord had a very mild expression.

I inquired if he could give us food.

" What would you like ? " he asked.

It is possible I let him notice that the one thing I did not like was the prospect of eating in this room. At all events he beckoned that we were to follow him. And he conducted us into a bedroom with two very stiff-looking beds, a large green stove and a table. As we took our seats at either side of it the landlord said that there was not much in the house. All he could give us was a soup with macaroni, then a piece of veal and then some cake. He also had a wine, he said, which was not very bad.

" Bring all those things," I begged him, " and as soon as possible. We are extremely hungry. We have walked from Turčiansky. It has been hard work in such a wind."

" I am famished," said Jozef, as he undid his belt.

" But, as for me, do not bring the veal, because I am a vegetarian."

It was not strange that this remark fell on me like a thunderbolt. I did not see the landlord going from the room. I did not see the room or Jozef. I was stunned.

We had to wait some minutes for the soup and Jozef spoke to me. I thought I heard him say that this must be the habitation of a Protestant, because there was a Bible in the room, in fact two Bibles. Then he spoke about the pictures which were family groups, the host's family, he presumed, and the Holy one.

" What is there to smile at ? " said Jozef.

" Have you always been a vegetarian ? " I asked.

CHAPTER V

THE grave landlord attended on us during the meal; and when he brought in the cake, a kind of shortbread, he went across to the other side of the room and fetched himself a chair. This he deposited at a small distance from our table.

"With permission," said he, as he sat down.

He made no remark while we were munching the shortbread. And when we expressed our appreciation of it he gazed at us as if his thoughts were far away.

I assured him that I was feeling much happier than when we were out on the road.

"Well, that is why you came," said he. And as he spoke these words he seemed to be sinking further and further from happiness. "It is the same with all of them," he said, "with all of them. The longer I stay here the more uncertain I am whether I ought to stay." He shivered. Then he lifted his right hand, he covered up his eyes with it.

We two looked at each other. Could it be that this man was a murderer and that we had arrived just at the hour of his repentance? What should we do? Should we do nothing?

Jozef pointed to his violin and I nodded. This

would serve to occupy some very awkward moments.

The landlord removed his hand from his face and, as Jozef took out the violin, he gazed at him in a dull sort of fashion.

I was wondering what Jozef would think it appropriate to play. Would he with one of those yearning gipsy melodies lure out a confession that was trembling on the brink?

" I am fond of music," said the landlord. " I am glad that you are going to play. Do you play to your companion while you walk along? "

" Well," I said, " we have not thought of that."

" Other pilgrims do it very often, but they travel in a larger crowd than you have done. Often they are fifteen or twenty, partly men and partly women."

" Where are they bound for? " I asked.

His lips were parted and he stared at us. " But— but surely you are pilgrims? " he said. " The holy well beside our church . . ."

I begged him to excuse our ignorance.

" They come from all over Slovakia," said the landlord, " and even from Poland."

Had he ever heard, I asked, about the man who was invited to support a mission to the heathen? He declined to do so; but if a heathen, he said, would call on him at his flat he would be pleased to do what he could in order to convert him.

" I see," said the landlord. " But this holy well

of ours is famous and we have a little book about it. There one reads about the miracles, how the priest who was also the guardian of the well caught a violent cold in the year 1886. So much did he suffer from an inflammation in his mouth and so much did it hurt him that for a period of two weeks he could neither sleep nor eat."

" After two weeks of that," said Jozef, " he must have been dead."

" But I myself," said the landlord quickly, " I do not believe in the little book. I am a Lutheran, you understand. What I am doing is to tell you the piece in that book, how the vicar of the parish suffered more and more ; at last he resolved that he would seek a sanctuary and the assistance he wanted, he would seek to gain those favours from God and the Virgin Mary. Therefore on the first of September of that year he commanded that water should be fetched for him out of the Virgin's well ; he drank a glass of it. And behold, the inflammation vanished there and then. He who—that is what is written in the little book— who early in the day could bear nothing in his mouth, at noon was absolutely cured. He had a monument erected on the spot—it is still there, we will go to see it. When would you like to go ? "

He was about to rise to his feet, but I explained to him that we were, both of us, very tired, and that we would prefer to listen to him.

" Why should you not rest yourselves ? And I,"

said the amiable landlord, " I will talk until you go to sleep."

" It is very good of you," quoth I. " Now does it not seem curious that the priest who was the guardian of the well did not avail himself of it as soon as he noticed the first symptoms ? "

While we were taking off our boots the landlord said that the priest had died a long time ago. Since then the local authorities had shown their interest. They were building a fine road up to the well—it used to be surrounded by trees. And what troubled him was that he was a Lutheran. He was gaining money from the pilgrims, although he did not accept the Virgin Mary, nor the well, nor anything. He did not believe in them, but he would soon be rich—not very rich, but rich enough—out of the Virgin and her well. What could he do ? . . . He looked so helpless and forlorn.

" Have you seen any miracles yourself ? " asked Jozef. " Because it seems to me that, if you have, you ought to enrol yourself behind the Virgin and leave off being a Lutheran."

" It is all very difficult," said the landlord. " I will go away, so that you can rest, and afterwards I will come back."

Jozef and I did not go to sleep, because as he looked up at the ceiling it made him think of a certain gipsy at Žilina. This man had inherited a house and the first thing he did was to make a hole in the ceiling, so that while he lay in bed he could watch the stars.

A thousand, thousand leagues appeared to separate the domesticity of the room in which we were lying and the room of that gipsy at Žilina. I turned to Jozef and I asked him if in his opinion his old race would ever be absorbed into the Slovaks.

On his lips there was the shadow of a smile. " If you go to a large town," he said, " like Košice, where two thousand gipsies live on the outskirts of the place in little wooden huts—but I talk as if Koišce had nothing but gipsies ! It is a town of 60,000 people, a prosperous town with the finest Gothic cathedral in Slovakia. And the market is wonderful ; I think there is nothing you cannot buy there. And General Šnejdarek commands the troops."

" But I thought," I said, " that your people are seldom called upon to do military service. What do you know about the army ? "

" I know that General Šnejdarek is a splendid man," he said. " He left the old Austro-Hungarian army— —I suppose he had difficulties as a patriotic Slav— he went to Africa and joined the Foreign Legion. He won promotion after promotion—he became an officer, the chief of a regiment—and one day, after an affair against the Arabs, he rode into Algiers at the head of his victorious troops—a lady leaned out of a window and hit him with a rose—that lady is now his wife. But what was I telling you about

Košice ? Yes, if you go there, to those little wooden huts, when the darkness falls, you will see some men in evening-clothes come out of those huts—sometimes when the entrance is like that they have to crawl out on all fours—throughout the day they have been as the other gipsies, dressed in rags and unclean. Well, are they absorbed by going to the hotels and making music ? . . . I must say," Jozef added, "that the people who are over this country do their best. In the Hungarian times a gipsy could be shot at sight and there was no more inquiry—perhaps not so much— than if a game-bird had been shot. We were looked on as vermin. Have you heard of the gipsy school at Užhorod ? It is the only one in the world. The gipsies built it themselves, just outside Užhorod on the edge of the town ashpit. The twenty-five . . ."

" But what," I interrupted, " what was the reason for building it there ? "

" Part of the ashpit is underneath the school and it does the gipsies no harm. Their twenty-five little houses are all around. One of them is where the headman lives ; they call him the gipsy mayor. When I looked at the school I found that his son was the only pupil with a pair of boots and the mayor is the only person who has a table in his house. You see, we are a nomad folk, ready to start off at any moment."

" But if those Užhorod gipsies were to go, what would happen to the school ? "

" As a matter of fact." said Jozef, " they are settling

5

down more than some people of that part who are
not gipsies at all. I mean the shepherds who spend
the warm months on the pasture lands, which are
very remote, and in the winter they likewise live in
lonely districts. By Czechoslovak law the children
are not obliged to attend a school if it is beyond four
kilometres away, though many of them go much
further. But I wanted to tell you of these shepherds
in the winter. They receive an itinerant schoolmaster who sets up his establishment in some stable
or outhouse. It is a hard life, because the teacher has,
every year, to begin again—the child has usually forgotten what he learned the previous winter."

" You told me," I reminded him, " that the Užhorod
gipsies built their own school-house."

" And they are very proud of it and of the bath in
the next room. Not merely the children wash their
bodies, for the parents have taken to following their
example."

" So that," I said, " they will be less and less inclined to wander ? "

" When the spring returns," said Jozef, " they long
to be out in the open, even if only in the neighbouring
woods."

" You need not be a gipsy," said I, " to feel like
that."

" I suppose not," said Jozef. " But shall I tell you
about their school ? I heard the teacher taking them
through a lesson in agriculture. They answered,

more or less accurately, what one has to do with a turnip field at various times of the year. Meanwhile the girls were having a needle-work lesson from a lady. The State provides the material and the thread—and the pupils are presented with the finished article. What a god-send that must be ! Particularly the boys were in a ragged condition, as one sees them all over Slovakia in the places where they do not have the advantage of a school. Many of them had their shirts open all the way down, for lack of buttons, several had their trousers held up by bits of string, I told you of their turnip lesson ; but what they love most is the lesson in music. A number of violins, provided by the State, hang from their hooks at the far end of the room. The boys are being taught to read the notes, instead of only playing by ear."

" Do you think that this will injure their wild gipsy strains ? " I asked.

" I think not," said Jozef.

" And so the school has been a success ? "

" Most certainly it has, for since its foundation not a single article has been stolen from it. There is such honesty as one would not have thought possible. But sometimes the people are in an awkward position. Not long ago the teacher happened to say that there was a shortage of wood for heating the bath water. So one or two of the scholars sacrificed their new honesty for the general good—they stole what was needed. Yes, they love their school. Very often the caretaker is knocked up at six in the morning. That is when the parents set out for their humble duties in the town—cleaning the streets, the lavatories and so forth—and the children much prefer to be in the school-room, where the lessons do not begin until eight o'clock, rather than in their own homes."

" If there is only one table. . . ."

" And for the children," said Jozef, " there are no beds. They sleep on the floor. And perhaps it is as well. We are not very civilized and after all these centuries we cannot, at a moment's notice, be like other people. Some of us, who lived at a place called Moldava, are lying in prison. They have been there for many months while the lawyers prepare the case. They have confessed to being cannibals."

" I have heard of it," I said.

" Whether it is true or not, they are making it easier for the judges by dying in prison—one of them has become insane and three have grown tuberculous—they cannot bear to be confined. Now in the prison they have central heating, which they had not dreamed of, and three meals a day, the first regular meals in their life ; but we are not as other people. Who knows," said Jozef, " if we ever shall be ? Perhaps that school at Užhorod will do something, perhaps of those thirty-three children a few will grow up to be like ordinary citizens." He sighed.

" Jozef," I said, " you have told me a good deal about some gipsy children I shall, I daresay, never see.

But of your own childhood you have told me
nothing."

" What is there to tell ? " said he. " We had no
school in those days—not that kind of school. But I
used to knock even before six in the morning. Have
you ever felt like that ? When all the space between
you and the lovely sky is full of troops of dancers and
they beckon to you and they take you with them over
the wet rocks and over the tall, misty trees and up
into the singing air. . . . There was I, outside the
tent, with everybody in the tent asleep. I stood and
listened to the world. How beautiful it was ! I had
no clothing on, except the gay wind and the sun-
beams. I was filled with a most magical delight and
with uncomprehended pain."

He stopped. He was not one of those who are
ashamed for having spoken from their heart.

" That was my school," said he, " the only school
I ever visited."

As we lay there upon the beds we heard some
noises from the public room, words of farewell that
seemed to be addressed to everyone and ponderous
boots that walked across the floor.

" I think the landlord will be coming back to us,"
said Jozef, " and what I have told you of my childhood is so little."

" It is more," I said, " than is contained in many of
the large books of biography."

He smiled. " But I would have been glad," said

he, " to tell you other recollections of the past. One day, for instance, I was most unhappy—I remember I was weeping, because a woman in a village gave me some cakes—they were very hard, but they were cakes and usually the village folk were not so kind. I can remember it as if it happened yesterday, how I wept because she gave me the cakes and afterwards, when I found that I could only eat five of them, I wept again. The woman was not looking on at the end of it, but I was angry with myself for being so feeble. . . . And one day when we pitched our camp beside another village and I went exploring down the street there was a stout woman on the bank of the river who was washing a small pig. She washed it with soap and it squealed as if it were being killed. Someone on my side of the river asked her why she did this ; she replied that it lived with them in the house and it was bitten—you could see the sore places on the pink back of it. And then the other person said it would be an act of benevolence if she would wash me. I ran away and they both laughed. I would have given anything if I could have rescued the pig. . . . That was an afternoon of excitement. When I advanced I met a flock of geese, just as one does in all the villages. But these, when they saw me, did not only thrust out their necks. They waddled at me as fast as they could and their eyes were the fiercest and most cruel I had seen. This made me scamper out of the village ; but when I was near the camp I walked, in fact I strolled, as if I

had been heroic. ' What are you so pale for ? ' someone shouted. Then I shouted back that I had had a
fight with geese and that they were enormously afraid
of me. . . . And now," said Jozef, rolling over so that
he faced me, " now it would be very nice indeed if you
will tell me all about yourself. I hope," he added in
an anxious voice, " that you are not angry. Maybe
I ought not to ask you."

" Jozef," I said, " you are very welcome to the story
of my life. And I will not pretend that it is dull. What
life is dull if we tell the truth ? I see that you agree
with me."

" That I . . . oh ! " he said, and he looked very
disarming, " my thoughts were somewhere else. I
was just thinking that we are so like each other."

" But you did not have a music-master," I said.

" That is true," said Jozef.

" A music-master who told you that it was no use
to continue."

Jozef threw out an exasperated arm. " The man
was wrong," he cried. " I will teach you myself."

" It is very good of you," said I, " but I will never
learn the violin."

" You *shall* learn ! " exclaimed Jozef. He was
leaning on his elbow and looking at me with drawn
features. " What you have to do," he said, " is only
to do as I show you."

" If that were possible ! "

" Of course it is possible. Shall we begin at once ? "

But at that moment the door opened and the land-lord reappeared. He said that, having heard us in the other room, it sounded as if we had had sufficient rest. Would it appeal to us, he asked, if he were now to take us to the well? This was the one thing in the village that we ought to see.

The landlord could not tell us very much about the well, that is to say what illnesses it cured. It was, he said, holy. That was all he knew. And doubt-less it could heal anything.

" If," said Jozef, as we started through the village, " if I had heard of it at Turčiansky, then. . . ."

" Do you mean to say," cried the scandalized land-lord, " . . . ."

" I am very sorry," said Jozef, " and especially so because I would have sent one of our customers. He is an excise official, a bachelor and so he takes his meals at the hotel. He is very deaf, which makes it necessary for him to have one of those ear-trumpets. You will scarcely believe me if I tell you that a waiter poured some food down the trumpet."

" The scoundrel was drunk," said the landlord.

" Not just then," said Jozef. " He was under notice to leave."

" That house over there," interrupted the landlord. He pointed to a building with a leaden roof.

" The house of an American," I said.

" Yes," said the landlord, " he is one of ours who has come back. We call him America. But," he turned to Jozef, " you were telling us about the ear-trumpet."

" That waiter," said Jozef, " was to leave in a day or so. And when he poured the lentils down the trumpet he stood there and laughed. So did everyone else."

" Is that so ? " said the landlord, who was walking between us. " But I know of one person who did not laugh, the owner of the trumpet."

" As soon," said Jozef, " as he saw what had happened he made a very good remark. ' This trumpet,' he said, ' has become a horn of plenty.' While he shook out the lentils onto his plate and brushed a few of them off his sleeve he kept on repeating, with evident pleasure, that his trumpet was a horn of plenty. His neighbour patted him on the back and everyone was delighted. The waiter would have poured down the rest of his lentils, but the trumpet, as I told you, was no longer in position. So the man did not know what to do."

The church, which was unassuming, came into sight when we rounded a corner ; in front of it there was a fairly large oblong space. Here, said the landlord, a market was held on two days of the week. This was not one of them. An old rubicund woman was the solitary merchant. By the church wall she had got a miscellaneous display of fruit and vegetables.

We were quite close to her when we suddenly perceived, on the other side of the wall, a middle-aged man who was kneeling. What struck us at first was

the wisp of straw which had been tied onto each of
his legs, so that his trousers would not be damaged ;
and indeed some such protection was necessary, for the
man moved onward. He was one of those devout
persons who walk round holy buildings on their knees.
But as he made his painful progress he was not engaged
in prayer, at any rate not when we arrived, for he took
off his hat and waved it at us. He did not present the
appearance of having in his mind any elevated or
unworldly thoughts.

" Good afternoon," he said with a pleasant smile.

" He is," said the landlord to us in a low voice, " he
is one of the pilgrims."

Meanwhile the woman of fruit and vegetables had
arisen from her chair—she was very corpulent—and
she came up to us. " Would you like to buy the man
some fruit ? " she said. " You would be doing a good
deed. This man is doing a very good one."

" Excuse me if I ask you," said the landlord to the
pilgrim, " but are you going round the church ? "

" That is so," he replied, " but I am no sinner. I
have got no crimes to expiate."

" Then," said Jozef, "you must be doing it for a
wager."

The man was amused at this notion. " Nothing of
the kind," he said. " I am going round the church—
when I get to that gravestone I shall have finished—
and it is not for any evil I have done. It is for the
future. You see, when I commit a transgression this

act will be put against it." There was a comfortable smile on his face.

" Well," remarked the old woman, " I have never heard of such a thing. It is quite usual," she said to Jozef and me, " for the pilgrims to go round the church in that way ; but they have always a transgression to repent of. What will he do, this man, if he has no sins ? All the time he will go up and down, he will search for a sin. Yes, that is how it is . . . suppose you paid me the money and not for my fruit, but for the fruit next month or next year or the year after that. And who ever heard of such a thing ? "

CHAPTER VI

WE became acquainted with America. It was while we were watching the marvel of a sunset. Jozef and the landlord and I sat upon a bench, leaning back against the uneven wall of the hostelry. And everywhere the sky was a magnificence, a gold and crimson glory. Had the gardener of the gods conceived a tulip ? We were more than half afraid of looking at such splendour. Then it seemed as if a rift was made in one of the great petals and behind it was another sort of gold, the stateliness of the departing sun.

" In such a place as this," said the landlord, " there is not much we can show you. But that man can tell you a good deal. I am so glad that he has come."

A few yards from us and already holding out his hand I saw a square-built, bearded individual who walked as if he were a sailor.

" He can tell you very many things," announced the landlord.

" Well, that is a fact," said the new arrival. After shaking hands with us—he had an air of being very much at peace with all the world—he asked if there was room for him upon the bench, and, with some little difficulty, we accommodated him between the landlord and myself.

Then the landlord, leaning round his friend and with a hand upon the broad knee of that person, introduced him to us. This, he said, was America. " He has that name," quoth the landlord, " because he has been over there. Of course he has another name as well . . . his name," I heard him say, " . . . you understand . . . our . traveller . . . so proud of him . . . because. . . ."

The pageant of the heavens had reached another stage. No longer was the whole sky covered by the gold and crimson hangings ; they were being drawn apart, so that the spaces of pale purple could be seen behind them. Here and there one saw the flickering of a star, which had to struggle lest it should be drowned.

" Are you listening to me ? " said the landlord. " This America of ours, he has sailed the seas, I tell you."

" Oh, but not all of them," said America, rather modestly.

" Perhaps not all of them," said the landlord. " Yet he has been a traveller in his time. When someone in the village wants a question answered with respect to the United States, they go to him. And he will do the same for you. What would you like to know ? "

" Thank you very much," I said, " and you too, sir," said I to the bearded man.

" Oh, that's all right," said he.

" But—will you let me think about it ? Just a moment," I pleaded.

Now the sun had gathered to itself a great deal of the crimson which was being thrown out of the sky. And in a world more dreary, with the colour of it more and more demolished, the grand sun went slowly and majestically and in gorgeous raiment to the grave.

" Nothing happens in our village," said the landlord. " So you can be thankful that America is here to talk to you."

A lonely tree that stood beyond the furthest habitation was receiving in its boughs the last rays of the sun. I did not know what kind of tree it was, but anyhow the brilliant foliage it carried is not often seen on earthly trees.

" For instance," said the landlord, " he can tell you the depth, exactly how many metres it has, that mine in Pennsylvania where he worked."

" And hard work it was," said America. " But I would not allow that to discourage me. No, sir. From the beginning of my time in the United States up to the time when I sailed back, there I was in the Pennsylvania mine. It is the deepest mine of any country."

" Do you hear that ? " asked the landlord. " I call it a fine piece of luck that we have such a man in our village. The very deepest mine, the number one mine of the whole country."

As a matter of fact we did obtain from America some information of interest. This occurred on the next day, a day of laughing sunshine, when he walked with us about half way to Orava.

I could see that he was disappointed, for we had not asked him anything about his Continent. And, so that he should not think too badly of us, I resolved to put some query to him.

Then it was that he began to talk : " We may be worthless people, we Americans," he said, " but there are some who win a triumph. Have you heard about that servant-girl who went from Prešov, down in East Slovakia ? It is a town which the Hungarians call Eperjes. There is a native of the town who made his fortune in the States and when he knew that the metal parts of the church organ had been commandeered in the war he promised his assistance. He gave them a little organ himself and he collected in America among the Slovaks for a large one, but only on condition that the people of the town would also help in the good work ; he wanted them to put in the stained windows. So the farmers made themselves responsible for one window and other artisans for a second one and so on— and a window just over the entrance was paid for by the servant girl. Before she emigrated she had been the servant of some rich Hungarian people—their name is Ghillany. They declined, although they are Catholics, to contribute towards the windows, and they gave no reason. It must be a curious feeling for them when they go out of the church and look up at the window."

By this time the road was starting to curl up into

the mountains, and I asked Jozef how they managed in the schools where the population is mixed.

" Well," said Jozef, " let me explain. For instance, there is a good-sized place called Velka Beresna, which is in Ruthenia, the province next to Slovakia. In the Hungarian days the judge, the district doctor, the notary and the teacher were Hungarian. Perhaps they had among them ten or twelve children, and there were about eighty or a hundred Ruthenian children. But there was only one school and that was Hungarian. What happens nowadays ? There are two villages, Minay and Homok, not far from Užhorod. Most of the population are Hungarian and they have their Hungarian school. Yet there are also some Czech children, whose fathers are officials. These are not favoured as the Hungarians favoured their own people in years gone by. No, these children have to get up very, very early so as to go by train to Užhorod, where is the nearest Czech school. And, by the by, the notary of Homok is an elderly Hungarian, one Kendelényi, of the old aristocracy, an agreeable and competent person, they told me, and even now—though our Republic has existed since 1918—he has a very small acquaintance with the State language."

America had halted. He was holding out his hand.

I thanked him for his company.

" All right, all right," he said. " And I hope you will give everyone as much pleasure as you have given me."

Despite the beard, his face had the sincerity that is in children.

But how complicated it all is ! The people for whose entertainment we have put ourselves to very little trouble are so often those who have the warmest gratitude.

" I have thought of something," said Jozef suddenly. " Perhaps you always meet the persons you want to meet. I am not sure," he added with diffidence, " but it came into my mind."

If any wayfarer had come along the road he would have been astonished at the spectacle of us three men. It was not merely that we stood there in the radiant sunshine and that we paid it no attention. But on what account, he would have asked, had we come to a stop and why were we gazing so earnestly at one another ?

" How can it be right as you say ? " asked America. " For I have always been willing to marry and never yet have I found a woman who was made for me. Sometimes I thought I had, but when I told them of it they disagreed with me." He looked so puzzled.

" It is not every woman," I replied, " who feels herself capable of being the wife of a prominent man. The landlord says you are one of the chief citizens."

" But," he assured us, " I would have been kind to them. Ah well, ah well. . . ." He sank into a reverie.

Meanwhile two lizards on a milestone had attracted Jozef. He was eyeing them with what one might call rapt amusement, for they clearly had much joy in one another. They would race—a brief and perpendicular performance—after which they turned their heads and it was obvious they were comparing notes.

"At any rate," said Jozef, "those two have each met the one thing they wanted to meet. But I intended it in this way—that a man is blind to the folk he does not wish to see and only sees the others."

Whereupon I remarked that he, at all events, seemed to have had the luck of meeting men of wisdom.

"As for being blind," said America, "it was only the other day that I was arguing with someone. He would have it that, both in towns and in the open country, one does not have adventures, one does not—how shall I say ?—find a drama being acted, perhaps with several persons, perhaps with one. He would have it that such things do not occur upon the main roads but beneath a gloomy archway or upon a bypath or else in a place where is no path at all. But you have only to keep your eyes open, I answered, and such things can be observed upon the main roads in the country or the towns. I hope your journey will be good."

"You are the sort of man," I said, "who is the proper kind of traveller. I wish you could have told us more about your own experience. But we will keep that for another time."

America was beaming at me. "In our own village,"

he said, " and right in the middle of it is a well. The wife of the owner of the shop, an old woman, was found in the well. She said her husband's young sister had thrown her in and so the sister was sentenced to five years. But she was lucky, she had for her lover the policeman and he occupied himself with the crime and he found, in the end, that the old woman had not been pushed by anyone, that she had thrown herself down the well, because she wanted to bring trouble to her husband's sister. She threw herself down and she nearly stayed there, because even her own servant did not recognize her screams and thought it was the devil. So you see what happens on the main roads."

Then America departed and we plodded onward, up and up the winding path. The philosophic views of our late comrade had impressed me very much, for they were so entirely unexpected. It was with some eagerness that I walked on and when we saw that, far away, there was a woman coming towards us with a perambulator, I felt sure that she would be the heroine of some romance, one whom we must at any cost engage in conversation. She perceived us, but this did not seem to modify her gait or manner. Placidly she was propelling down the road that squeaky perambulator, for the noise it made was such that I could not imagine how the child could sleep.

Perhaps it had been so ingeniously contrived in order that the lamentations of this miserable infant should be drowned. The woman probably had kidnapped some rich farmer's offspring. There was not a house in sight and why should anyone, if lawfully inclined, bring out her perambulator to the open country ? Some dark deed was being done.

By this time the woman had come very close to us and she displayed no hesitation. We would have a callous individual to deal with. It did not occur to me, I must confess, that she might simply have been going with her child to pay a visit in a neighbouring village ; I should not have overlooked this possibility, because the woman was of robust build.

No, I felt certain that she was an evil-doer. As she reached us, of her own accord she stopped the perambulator and she greeted us. It was a most disarming smile. How beautiful she was ! The straw-coloured hair peeped out from the white kerchief and this did not conceal her noble brow. Presumably she was what one calls a woman of the people, and yet with such a brow and with such calm, blue eyes and such delightful lips and such a dear, decided chin, one could not but regard it as incongruous to see her dressed in peasant's clothing.

" Would you like to buy some eggs ? " she asked us.

There was nothing in the perambulator but about a score of eggs.

" And is it worth your while," I asked, " to go so far ? "

" If they do not give a good price down there, then I shall go," she said, " to Turčiansky."

I was gazing at her when I heard the voice of Jozef. He proposed to walk on round the hair-pin corner and if he could find a pleasant spot he would sit down to rest.

" But as for you," I said to this remarkable young woman, " do you walk without a rest to Turčiansky ? "

" Would you like," she said again, " to buy some eggs ? They are extremely fresh."

" I am not sure," I said. " Supposing we discuss the question."

Just before the road bent round there was a growth of heather. One could sit on it and lean one's back against the earth quite comfortably. This I demonstrated.

" We may be a little time in bargaining," I said, " and why not rest our feet ? "

She nodded and, when she had put a stone behind one of the perambulator's wheels, she came across to where I was and sat down at my side.

" If," she began, " you were from this part of the country, you would know me. I go up and down with eggs."

" And as it is," I said, " I do not even know your name."

" It is Zuzanna."

Her two hands lay folded in her lap. The freckles on the back of them were fascinating.

" Yes," quoth she, " it is a good business, the sale of eggs."

" I should have thought," said I, " that in a farming country they would not have needed them from elsewhere. What a splendid place this is," I said. " We can see anyone for miles away and my companion, who has gone ahead, will see them coming down the hill and he will warn us, I am sure."

" You understand," she started to explain, " a town like Turčiansky has to buy its eggs and so I go there to the market. It is a long walk."

" My poor little girl," I said, " I will take all your eggs. So let us think no more about your business worries and all that."

Zuzanna laughed. " How can you take them all ? " she asked. " They are not hard-boiled. They are fresh, as I have told you, and . . ."

" I do not care," I said. " How weary you must be. Lean back and close your eyes."

" Thank you very much," said she," but indeed I am not weary." She continued to sit bolt upright. " What were we talking of ? . . . Ah yes, about the eggs."

" Zuzanna," I said, " who knows if I shall ever see you again ? "

" That is why "—she did not seem to notice that my arm had now encircled her—" that is why," she said, " we will lose no more time. We are not backward in this country, we are backward no longer. But I will give you an example. What are you smiling at ? Well, here is an example. More and more the roads are filled with motor-cars and more and more they kill my hens."

" You should make them pay for it," I told her.

" But they kill them legally," she answered, " for a hen has got no right to be upon the road. We should have children looking after them. And now the children have to go to school, so that they cannot watch the hens. I wonder sometimes what will happen first—will there be a breed of hens who are accustomed to the motor-cars or will that breed not come, at any rate to me, because their mothers have all died ? "

While she was discoursing in this fashion my friend Jozef on the road above had taken out his violin. The first few bars of a delicious serenade had grown into an ecstasy of love.

" Your friend plays very well," she said.

The worthy Jozef, it was evident, had sat him down discreetly where he could not hear our conversation and he fancied that what he was playing was appropriate.

" The times have brought the motor-car," she said, " but they have also brought us something good. We used to have a single goat and now we have two little cows. I treat them very well. One can do much with kindness."

" It all depends," said I.

" But what is making you so sad ? " asked Zuzanna. " Oh, perhaps the music. It is very mournful, what he plays."

I told her that it was a passage in a love-song. As I spoke I pressed her to me, but at that same moment she arose and thus I had to disengage my arm.

" It has been very nice," she said, as she looked down on me. " It has been nice to have a talk about these things. In other days we had no land at all and now we have some land. And gentlemen have told us that we will be granted an allowance of a new kind of manure. All the fields will benefit, they say, when——"

" Oh, bother the manure ! "

Her lovely lips were parted as she stared at me. " But . . . but . . . do you not wish well to Slovakia ? " she asked.

I made a gesture.

" Yes, of course you do. And you would understand that the manure is needed, you would understand if you had thought about it all as much as I have."

" Tell me this," I said, as I got up. " How comes it that you know so much ? "

" My brother says it is unjust to blame the Government for doing nothing. They have done a great deal, on the contrary."

" I hope," I said, " that they are grateful to you for supporting them. I never met a girl so well-informed."

" But I could tell you more," she offered. " For example would you like to know what the manure is going to do for us ? "

" It is very kind of you," I said, " but . . ."

" Then I shall be able to go to Turčiansky and buy one of those beautiful kerchiefs for my head, a white one with coloured flowers all round it."

" So you are an optimist," I said, " with regard to Slovakia ? "

She was pushing the stone from under the wheel of the perambulator. And at the same time she took a couple of eggs from the interior and held them out to me.

" No, no, I will not accept any money," she said, " because I have enjoyed so thoroughly our little conversation. I shall think of it as I go down the hill."

" And I shall think of it as I go on to Orava. You can be sure of that," I said.

Then she took out two other eggs and asked me to deliver them to my companion, for she had enjoyed his music very much.

CHAPTER VII

THAT night we slept at Orava. It is the chief place, though little more than a hamlet, of the old department of Orava. Range after range of wooded mountains, with green places scattered here and there among them, take up most of this unprosperous region, which is in such contrast with the moderately fertile plain of Turčiansky and the still more fertile southern belt. There is only one railway line which passes through it, a single line that finishes at the Polish frontier ; but even this one line has not much work to do, since Orava's requirements are very modest and she has nothing save her wood to send into the outer world.

These facts we ascertained while we were sitting round a gorgeous fire with two or three officials. They have the administration of the castle, which is uninhabited, and of the forests that belong to it. These forests, on the other hand, are populated by the small, brown bear and by the wolf and the wild boar, a grisly, uncouth animal except when he comes to you on a dish with cranberries or else a sauce of roses. As we sat around the fire we were not waiting for a meat but for the special kind of fish whose name I have forgotten. And I shall make no inquiries—we were told that it was excellent and luscious, an alluring fish that one could only find in Orava's main river, which descends in turbulence from Poland. But when we gathered round the table, those forestry officials, Jozef and myself, I thought that Orava, poor as she is, could well afford to do without that fish. Perhaps the texture of it was not quite so rough as I imagined and perhaps it was not wholly savourless, but those officials had been ultra-patriotic, they had celebrated it in far too lyric language.

Nevertheless, what with one thing and another, we stayed for well over an hour in that warm dining-room. It had astonished us to find at Orava so modern and so roomy an hotel. It was, we were told, in the centre of the place and from the circumference to the centre had taken us about two minutes. Daylight was already gone, so that we had made no attempt to see the castle.

"But for what reason," said one of the foresters, "do you think that they have such a fine hotel? It is because of the tourists."

Yet, for all I knew, the tourists might be persons who did not share my taste with regard to fish. I would not allow myself to fall in love with the castle until I had seen it.

"I will look at your castle to-morrow," I said.

The forester dissented. "It must be seen," he urged, "by night. There is a moon. Come out with me, I beg of you."

There was, we found, a rather feeble moon, but quite

sufficient, said the forester. He walked in front of us to point out certain puddles in the road, which we would not have noticed, for the few illuminated windows of the cottages and the occasional electric street lamps did not greatly help the moon.

There was a dark mass, a tremendous cliff that rose at our left hand and blotted out a portion of the sky. The vast, black wall made the remaining part appear, by contrast, fairly light ; it was a tattered and a furtive lightness, with the clouds prevailing mostly, though in places they were wounded into opalescence.

" Up there on the cliff it stands," our guide announced.

More than three hundred and fifty feet above us they had built a fortress in the thirteenth century. We could distinguish nothing, for the moment, but a spread of black, as if it were the wing of some obscene, huge vulture, on the summit. Then the moon emerged and we beheld, high over us, a piece which clearly had been built by man.

" There used to be great eagles," said our guide, " but now the brood in Orava does not compare with them."

How disdainfully those eagles must have looked upon the builders who were venturing to thrust a wall into the air, into the eagles' element.

A sudden touch of moonlight and the wall became a vessel, a black vessel sailing out into . . . .

" What do you think of it ? " inquired the forester.

" Are you not glad you came ? And on the slope of the cliff—you can scarcely see them—are the later buildings of the castle, which were added in the four-teenth and the fifteenth centuries."

To talk of centuries on such a night ! We stood outside them and we saw them drift away. And the black vessel sailed into eternity.

" To-morrow," said the forester, " you must look at everything. Yet there is not much to be seen, because it was a fortress, not a dwelling-place. But Count George Thurzo, the Palatine, lived here and was buried here, I think in 1616."

When Jozef and I returned to our room—a spacious apartment—and undressed ourselves he uttered not a word. But after I had been asleep an hour or two I was awakened—in my dream a vessel had been leaving a long, silver trail—which turned to melody— and Jozef was there, seated on the window-sill, the moonlight pouring over him and his beloved violin. He was translating into music what we two had seen that night.

As he perceived that I was watching him he looked embarrassed, while his fingers fell into a Slovak folk-song.

" It awakened me," I said, " your folk-song. Do not play it over me when I am dead—my heart would break."

He was relieved that I, apparently, had not heard anything of what he played before. And as he got off from the window-sill and came towards me he continued with his playing.

" Let us have another one," he said, " before we go to sleep. You remember the *Neozenim sa ?* "

Then, as his bow danced up and down, he sang the well-known, merry tale of the poor suitor who would not go courting in the fall, for then—I know not why particularly then—you would remark the holes in his jacket ; he would refrain in the winter, since he had no furs and in the moist days of the spring he likewise would deny himself, because his boots would not endure the mud. But what he proposed to do was to go courting in the summer ; and the rest of the song paints a delightful sketch of a summer landscape, which the young man is unable—and we are unable —to resist. He declares in a burst of confidence that he will make love to a girl in Sharish and that her name will be Marisha and that her eyes will be grey and full of solace, while her complexion will be—as one would expect—rosy and white, and her heart will throb for him alone.

After all the agitations Orava had given us, that folk-song made the night more tranquil. And—the hotel did not boast many carpets—neither foresters nor servants of the house made a self-satisfied, relentless impact on the flooring. Consequently we did not awaken till it was broad daylight.

" Good morning," said Jozef. " The salami stinks."

" Good morning," said I.

There was my olive-hued companion sitting up in bed, his hair in great disorder and his brow all furrowed with perplexity.

" Well, if it stinks," I said, " you must throw it away."

" That is what I want to consult you about," said Jozef. " I am not sure if it is bad enough. Will you . . ." He was getting out of bed, the sausage in his hand.

" Throw it out of the window ! " I ordered him.

One of the advantages of sleeping in the same room as a gipsy is that he has no objection to an open window. But I will admit that Jozef is the one gipsy with whom I have slept ; and if anyone travelling in Slovakia does me the compliment of using this book as a guide I must warn him that I cannot guarantee the nocturnal behaviour of all the gipsies. It is very likely that the average one, if he has to reconcile himself to a room of which the ceiling is unprovided with a hole through which one can study the stars, it is very likely that if he finds that the air is unable to enter in this fashion of his ancestors, he will prevent it from doing so through other openings.

" But perhaps," said Jozef, " perhaps . . ."

I had taken refuge underneath the feather-bed. They say that the Sicilians are of all people the most talented in the art of making oneself understood by gesture. But I doubt if even a Sicilian, handicapped by a feather-bed, would be capable of eloquence.

It is true that what I desired to convey to Jozef was not intricate. I merely wished to tell him that I had no thoughts of starting on a controversy and that I was quite prepared to accept his verdict on the sausage and that, this being so, I trusted he would carry out the sentence with no more delay.

Previous to this episode I had been wont to cavil at feather-beds. And it is not to be denied that they possess too little elasticity—you either have one on the top of you or you have not ; it is impossible to make adjustments in accordance with the temperature and yours, as one can do with sheets and blankets and eiderdowns. Nevertheless I uttered a most solemn vow—with Jozef there beside me—that henceforward I would never entertain the slightest sentiment which could be labelled anti-feather-bed. For I could smell the foulness of that sausage, and if it could penetrate to where I lay it must have been extremely virulent.

Oh, why did Jozef hesitate ? The noxious odour was discovering all kinds of passages to my recess. But then—and I thanked Heaven for it—Jozef's sagacity became predominant. He recognized that the salami had to be discarded and that time, in this case, was the essence of the contract. Out it flew. We both of us, when we reviewed the situation, felt that Orava might very well be hurt. We had insinuated ourselves into the little place, we had derived much benefit—save from the fish—and in return we

had behaved abominably. At that very instant the
salami might be causing damage—a rash dog or a
human might be taking their last earthly meal. We
hurried to the window—all was quiet and we could not
see where the red terror lay.

" We shall have to burn it," I said. Let me hope
that I did not look arrogant, but after all we do not
have that wondrous feeling of elation more than half
a dozen times—and some of us not even that—between the cradle and the grave, that we are born to
be supreme commanders-in-chief. A poet, it may be,
has died in most of us ; but the commander has more
toughness. Every now and then he shows that he is
perfectly alive and lo ! how grand it is to feel that—if
our circumstances had been different—Alexander,
Cæsar and Napoleon would have received a modern
compeer. In my own case there was more approxima-
tion to the Russian general who foiled Napoleon at
Moscow. He and I . . .

" But will it burn ? " asked Jozef. " You are
looking confident enough, but . . ." He struck his
leg.

And so he likewise had a great idea ! That we two
should have come together, it was splendid.

Jozef's face was a broad smile. " It may explode,"
he said. " That would be a good end for it. Yes, I
must tell you of an affair in the war, when I was in a
motor-cycle section. One of my comrades had a
salami, in case we should ever run short of food. It

7

was packed up in a roll of brown cardboard and fastened to the framework of his bicycle, so that the sergeant would not notice it. We had to do reconnoitring, of course, which took us far away from the column ; but we always, at that period, had enough to eat and the man with the salami said that he would save it up. We asked him sometimes for a piece, but he refused. ' The time for it will come,' he said. And one day we were in a forest with the enemy quite near to us. We had put our bicycles against the trees and we ourselves were lying in the undergrowth. Then suddenly there was a horrible explosion and we cursed the petrol-tank. Now the Russians would know everything. But, as it turned out, their advance guards thought it was a bomb—they ran back and made some report—hardly any of the men behind them had a rifle—you know how it often was in the Russian army. So they scattered through the forest and—as we afterwards heard—they had all kinds of tales about a fierce attack. There was no *morale* among the troops in that part of the front—they retreated in disorder— it became a panic—and our own men were able to advance more than two leagues. I forgot to tell you that it was all due to the salami. It fermented and the skin could not contain the gases. Our colonel was decorated."

We resolved to dress at once. To leave the sausage out there in the open and not warn the people would be criminal.

But as we stepped out of the room, we found a large, weather-beaten lady sitting in the corridor. From the basket of linen at her side we knew that she was the laundrywoman. At that moment she had several papers on her lap, another one she was examining, what time she scowled.

" Have you ever,"—she addressed us as we appeared —" have you ever seen such tiresomeness ? One party and then another sends me them."

" Your duty," I said, " as a citizen of this. . . ."

" They have found out my name, Berta Gasparik," she said. " Oh, I wish they would leave me in peace. Besides, I am not one of those who can read. Therefore it is not possible for me to know what they are promising. And I have to vote or I shall be punished." She looked as if these worries were too much for her.

" They did not have to vote before the war," said Jozef, " not the men and not the women."

" Oh, before the war," she moaned, " they never bothered you. And those who voted could get drunk at least. But now they close the drinking-shops. I am unhappy in this land."

" Good-bye," said Jozef, as he drew me to the stairs. " There is more happiness," he said, " than we used to have. Now let us find the sausage."

But we had not searched more than two minutes in among the stones and the long grass beside the river when a forester espied us and approached. He reassured himself that we had spent a good night.

" And what are you doing now ? " he asked.

What could we say ?

" It seems to me," quoth the forester, " that you are looking for something."

" We," said Jozef, " we thought that nowadays there is more happiness in . . ."

" Of all the strange folk ! " cried the forester. " You get up in the morning and you hunt for happiness. I wish you luck."

" You do not understand," said Jozef. " I will explain it to you."

The forester made a ceremonial bow. " You are a public benefactor," he said, " and if anyone deserves a statue . . . but there is one thing I certainly do not understand. You neither of you have a happy aspect. But no, I suppose it is natural. People must be unhappy before they go in search of happiness."

Then Jozef came quite close to the forester and laid a hand upon his arm. " Will you please listen to me ? " he said in an earnest voice. " We were not talking of our own happiness. I was putting forward to my friend that now the people in this country are happier than they used to be."

It took a moment or two for this to sink into the forester. " Come," he said, " let us go to the castle, and on the road I will tell you a story. Do you know Bishop Blaha," he asked me, " the bishop of Banska Bistrica ? He is a man of the world, a delightful man."

The forester was already a step or two away from us. We hastily glanced round, but as I could not smell the sausage I consoled myself by thinking that it must have fallen in the river and been swept along. We put ourselves at either side of the forester and walked with him in the direction of the castle.

" Bishop Blaha told me this," he said, " that when President Masaryk went to Bratislava a year or two after the beginning of the Republic, a series of deputations arrived at Government House. The Governor was Mr. Mičura, an estimable man. He had fixed up the whole programme, but it was modified. A German pastor made a speech that was not on the list and the President himself made an impromptu reply. What other country has a ruler capable of doing such a thing ? And among the clerical representatives were Roman Catholics and Lutherans and Jews. It was noticed that the President conferred with the Jews—two dignified old gentlemen—longer than with the others. And when all the functions were over and the President and his party, including the Governor, were going north in the special train, then after a while His Excellency said he would relate what had passed between himself and the Jews. There was a twinkle in his eye. The Governor begged him to desist, but Masaryk averred that this was impossible. I ought to tell you," said the forester, " that our Jews, when they talk German, have the custom of adding the word ' Leben ' which means life, at the end of a word by way of endearment, because life is the greatest gift. This ' Leben ' or ' life ' one may translate by the word ' darling '. Well, the President asked them if they were happy in Czecho-slovakia. ' Mr. President-darling,' they answered, ' no one could be happier than we are in this land. There is no injustice any longer, now that we have Mr. Mičura-darling as Governor. Everyone can have an audience. If we have any representations to make, Governor Mičura-darling listens to them and attends to them. In fact we have only one request.' ' And what is that ? ' asked His Excellency. ' Oh, President-darling,' they said, ' will you please be so good as to make arrangements so that the Governor-darling shall stay here for a hundred years ? ' ''

By this time we had passed under the prison-like entrance to the castle, after which one proceeds through a tunnel with a slightly curved roof. Had we been unwelcome visitors and in the Middle Ages we would have gone forward with the utmost delicacy, lest through various apertures we be involved in boiling lead. This tunnel, that curves upward, brings one out at last into an oblong space, with sky above it.

In one angle is the dwelling of the custodian, an amiable, youngish man with a bunch of keys. But what you chiefly remember concerning him are his colossal duck and drake. They spend their lives in this little courtyard, far above the river. Thus they exercise themselves but sparingly ; indeed almost the sole activity of the duck is the laying of eggs. As for the drake, it is difficult to think how he contrives to spend his days. He and the wife, removed from the water, their element, the water which is to them, amongst other things, a nuptial couch, have been unable to rear a family. Now and then the corpulent couple must have sighed when they reflected on this; but maybe they are philosophers; at any rate their bodies testify that they do not grieve overmuch.

" You see," said the forester, " this castle was a fortress, not a dwelling-place, and so the architecture of it is not ornamental."

Here and there the plain, high, yellow walls relax into a charming balcony. One staircase—that which leads out of the courtyard of the ducks—might have been brought from Florence. Possibly an owner of this fortress had been told of that Bohemian monarch with an English wife and was just as anxious to be good to his. That monarch was so bountiful a husband that he ordered quantities of nightingales for a bleak home of his. They were to sit amid the trees and sing outside the windows of the Englishwoman. How he managed to persuade them not to fly from there can only be conjectured. And to Orava, instead of nightingales, there came, one thinks, a young Italian artist. Did he please the lady all too well, so that his body was flung down from the grim walls ? We can but speculate. But the majority of ladies would not have remained insensible to the great difference between this artist and the downright lords of Orava. One can but speculate. The chronicles say not a word.

We climbed that beautiful, old staircase and turned to the left into a room where we perceived what is the most enthralling sight in the whole castle. A glass case against the wall exhibits the two garments of George Thurzo, Count and Palatine, who died in 1611. What he favoured most was brown and gold brocade. They buried him in a long sleeveless robe of it and then an outer cloak of that material, with sleeves. The Count lay in his coffin for three hundred years ; they opened it and of George Thurzo, Count and Palatine, all that remained were a few particles of dust. One elbow of the sumptuous brocade allowed the daylight to come through it. Otherwise you can discern no traces of dilapidation. Also there is nowhere any label with the tailor's name.

CHAPTER VIII

It is to be feared that George Thurzo, being a Protestant, would not meet with the approval of Monsignor Hlinka. One cannot be very long in Slovakia before hearing the name of this prominent prelate. And the chances are that he is being advertised to make a most important speech on Sunday next. He is the leader of the Hlinka Party, otherwise the Slovak People's Party, which aims at representing all the Slovaks, at any rate the eighty-five per cent of them who are Roman Catholics.

Monsignor Hlinka's headquarters are at Ružomberok, where he went to school some sixty years ago, for he was born of peasant stock in a neighbouring village. Ružomberok is a fair-sized town, with textile and other industries. It is delighted, we were told, to honour Hlinka. But the Monsignor is in the habit of rushing hither and thither, all over the province and of spending several days a week in Prague, the capital of the Republic, when Parliament is in session.

At a place called Kubin, a straggling sort of townlet, we were told that it would be advisable to leave the road which runs beside the railway, since there is a shorter one across the hills to Ružomberok. We were likewise told a few more tales of Hlinka. Our inform-

ant was the local priest, an elderly gentleman whose
life was surely more unspotted than his clothes.
He stated that the Monsignor was the most patriotic
person in Slovakia, that he had always felt himself
to be a Slovak, and that under the Hungarian régime
he had spent four years in prison at Szeged.

" He is a great man," said the priest, " and we love
him. He is a great man, a great orator."

We were naturally most anxious not to miss him at
Ružomberok. So the priest, who had in his pocket the
current copy of Hlinka's newspaper, was kind enough
to take it out and adjust his spectacles.

Jozef and I sat on a bench beside him, there in the
exiguous but shady park. I was glad that Slovak
newspapers are likewise exiguous, for the good man,
moving his hairy forefinger along each line, began at
the beginning of the first column and proceeded to
plough steadily through the entire paper.

When he had reached the middle of the third column
—which I saw was devoted to a discussion of the
prospects of the year's vintage in Slovakia—I ventured
to suggest that the movements of the Monsignor would
be recorded in another column.

Thereupon the priest, after pushing his spectacles
an inch down his nose and looking at me over the top
of them, after looking at me for a while with gravity,
consented.

" It is very good of you," I said, " to take this
trouble."

" Oh," said he with a bland smile, " you need not thank me till I have succeeded. Now let me resume." He opened the paper and folded it in such a way that he could read the second page. He settled himself comfortably down to do so.

Then a motor-car came down the road and behind it, for some reason or other, was a dog tied by a rope. He was a large animal and clearly he was not distressed by having to go quickly. What distressed him, one could see from his harassed features, was the fact that multitudes of other dogs had loitered by the wayside trees or haply by the corner-stone of houses, whereas he was being forced to go without a tribute by. His was a tragedy of speed, ours was the opposite, for we were more or less compelled to wait upon that old priest's pleasure.

" Oho ! " he ejaculated.

" Is it there ? " I asked.

" Will you please listen ? You have heard about those one hundred and thirty-six clergymen of the next diocese, of Košice, who have protested to their bishop ? Here it speaks about them. What they want is that the Monsignor should be restrained from all activities whatever in the diocese. How could they dare it ? But I snap my fingers at them."

" Is that," I asked, " what the bishop did ? "

A shadow fell upon the old man's face. " Up to the present," he replied, " the bishop has not answered them."

" With such a popular man as the Monsignor," I said, " it may be difficult . . ."

" Yes," cried the priest, " they should be sent to Hell. What insolence ! To try to curb the Monsignor ! To criticize him ! As if he were not entitled to say what he likes."

" What is it," I asked, " that those clergymen did not like ? It must be something rather serious."

" Those clergymen ! " His voice was trembling with disgust. " Surely it is their sacred obligation to belong to the Hlinka Party. And if they do not, if they belong to the Agrarian Party or the Christian Socialist Party or any other one, then Hlinka goes to their parishioners and gives a warning. He tells them not to be obedient to their priest."

" He says that," I asked, " to those simple folk ? "

The old man turned sharply towards me. " Sir," he said, " you do not seem to realize that Hlinka is a patriot. That is why he spent four years in the prison of Szeged."

" And those one hundred and thirty-six clerics," I said, " are unpatriotic ? "

" They are Hungarians ! . . . You look surprised. Well, if they are not Hungarians," said he, " they are . . . they are. . . . What I wish to know is," he said in a petulant tone, " why can't they be faithful to the Hlinka Party ? It is the true Party for a Slovak. On its banner is inscribed the Catholic Church and, below that, Slovakia. What can be more suitable for a Slovak who is really honest, a God-fearing Slovak ? "

" You do not hold with those Parties," I said, " like the Agrarian, which extend over the whole Republic ? "

" I do not, for we are Slovaks. That is quite enough. And if the Monsignor chooses to talk politics during a sermon, I say it is not only right, it is perfectly right."

For some little time the old clergyman had been waving his newspaper to and fro in front of Jozef. This did not enable my good friend to read it. But at last he caught sight of the paragraph, by lucky chance, in which it said that Hlinka on that very day would unveil a monument to the Virgin Mary at a village on the Polish frontier.

" We must do something for those people," said the cleric. " They lived in Paradise after the war, when the fate of that strip of land was going to be decided by the plebiscite. What we did not do to have their votes ! Sugar and more sugar and other things we gave them. The Poles gave them petrol. And neither of us made them do military service. But when that period was over they were not satisfied to be treated like everyone else."

Meanwhile the agile Jozef had managed to read the next few words of that paragraph, namely that the Monsignor would go back in the afternoon to Ružom-berok.

Yes, said the priest, he would certainly drive across the high land, so that if we cared to walk ahead he would overtake us. All that we would have to do would be to look out for a car with a double cross on the top of the radiator. And the Monsignor would be charmed to take us on to Ružomberok.

" You will," said the old cleric with a radiant face, " I am sure that you will find him absolutely sympathetic."

As we rose, I said I would not fail to tell the Monsignor of a devotion he could count upon in Kubin.

" Well," said the old man, " I would die for him. And now God-speed to you. You cannot miss the road."

We struck out energetically and from Kubin we did not take long before we had attained the first and then the second village. Gradually we began to leave the level ground behind us. This was not a new road and in order to climb up the hills it went the shortest way. Thus our advance became laborious. Not merely was the gradient a severe one, but there was a wind which, owing to the absence of all trees and other obstacles, was hard to battle with. The land appeared to be an endless field of pasture, with no boundary marks upon it.

We did not meet any travellers, but after a considerable time we saw a flock of sheep and presently we noticed that two boys were sitting on the roadside.

They got up as we approached. The wind was making merry with their rags and with the flaxen curls of one of them. The other one, who was the smaller and whose clothing was, if possible, more ragged, had upon his head the remnants of a hat.

They stood there gazing at us and they made no secret of it that we interested them. Nay more, the curly head found us amusing.

" Tell me," I began, " where do you live ? I have not seen a house for a long time."

The younger boy looked at his comrade, who, though still amused, was obviously giving my inquiry his consideration. Should he answer me or not ? Would it be dangerous if he revealed his domicile ?

" How far away is it ? " I said.

By this time he had ceased to be amused, for which I didn't blame him.

" Far," said he. And from the jerk with which he shut his mouth I did not think it would be profitable to continue on this track. Whether his employer or his father had something to hide or whether the boy imagined I was one of the new-fangled officials who would drag him off to school or whether he was too much of a little savage to allow his privacy to be invaded—anyhow my question had not pleased him.

Then it was that Jozef took his violin out of the case and started playing on the windy hillside. The effect was instantaneous. The boys were, both of them, enthralled.

But while Jozef still was in the midst of it the elder lad, although I had not seen him take his eyes from Jozef's face, became aware that several of his sheep had strayed. He bent down, seized a stick and darted off. When he returned, the task accomplished very thoroughly and very swiftly, he resumed his place beside his little friend.

They stared at Jozef when he stopped. They were completely conquered. The one movement which they made was when the younger boy put up his hand to keep that relic of a hat upon his head.

A more appreciative audience one could not have ; and Jozef, grave with happiness, launched out into another piece.

This time again there was an interruption. None of us—the wind was powerful—had heard the car until it was quite close. And then we saw two persons disembark, a very handsome, elderly ecclesiastic and a layman, whose exterior was quite prosaic.

" May we join you ? " asked the Monsignor. " My name is Hlinka. This is my director."

When we had exchanged our greetings, Hlinka said that he had come through Kubin and that he had learned about us from the priest. Of course we must go on with them to Ružomberok. It was a fair distance. After the wild upland you descended and, once in the valley, you had got to pass through villages and a fine gorge and then another village, which was Lutheran.

" You always recognize a Lutheran village," he said, " because it has no children, very few children. But the Catholic villages . . . you boys are good Catholics ? "

" Yes," murmured the elder one.

" That is right ! That is right ! Never be a Hussite and a freethinker."

Even as he spoke he was examining the countryside. Then he let me see his splendid profile as he turned to the director.

" Yes, about ten minutes from here," said the director. " Just across that field and down a steep incline."

" I thought it was ! " cried Hlinka. " Gentlemen," said he, " will you go fishing with us ? The Hungarians gave me four years of prison at Szeged and, all that time, I had no fishing. Now I am an old man."

" You are more vigorous than I am," said the director, " and I am only middle-aged."

Hlinka's blue eyes sparkled as he thanked his lay companion. " Nevertheless," he said, " I do not like to lose more time. It is enough to lose four years. And so," he told us, " I have my fishing equipment in the car and my friend likewise. We have two pairs of waders. One, with your permission, I will wear. Which of you gentlemen would like a little sport ? "

It was agreed that Jozef should try his luck. Therefore he went with Hlinka to the car, while the director remained with me. He took the opportunity of informing me as to his directorship. At Ružomberok were the enterprises of the Monsignor and his associates—a bank, a printing-press, an orphanage and now the house of Slovak culture.

" There are some," he said, " who call it a hotel, but it is more than that. We have two cinema-halls and a gymnasium and a nice room for lectures and a children's room. Also it is the best hotel from one end of Slovakia to the other. It is our policy to make no difference between Slovaks and Hungarians and Germans—every Catholic is welcome."

" On the way to the monasteries of Mount Athos," I said, " there is a Greek hamlet by the sea and there one sometimes spends the night. It has a hostelry, a picturesque sort of place, and the proprietor looks at you before he makes up his mind whether he will or will not take you in. If he thinks that you are dis-agreeable he shakes his head."

" I hope," said the director, " that . . ."

" We were invited to a private house," I answered him. " But do you mean at your hotel to take in none who are not Catholics ? "

He said that he had only been referring to the social side, those who would use, for instance, the gymnasium. " Ružomberok is a town," he said, " which makes a Slovak heart to throb. When Hlinka promenades the streets his hand is kissed continually by the women, old and young, while the good men take off their hats. You know that he spent four years in the gaol at Szeged ? "

" Yes, I know of that," I said.

" He is the greatest . . . here he is ! "

Out of the car came Jozef and his host, arrayed as

fishermen. Hung from their shoulders, each had got a basket of an optimistic size. The rods they were adjusting as they walked.

" This is the time of day," said Hlinka, " when one catches fish. They go in search of supper."

" He is wonderful, our chief," said the director. " All the intricacies, all the subtleties regarding fish are known to him."

We started for the river. And the Monsignor said, with a rueful smile, that if he knew so much about the fish he ought to be ashamed of never catching more than one or two.

" Oh, that is a mere accident," quoth the director. " You throw out your arms—I daresay you are practising a speech."

" How foolish of me ! " said the Monsignor.

" No, not at all," said the director. " When Demosthenes was practising he strode beside the sea and never caught a single fish. But you—well, now and then you catch one."

Then he noticed that the two lads, with their flock in front of them, were coming after us. He was uncertain whether he would laugh or scold them.

I fell back and asked the curly-headed one why he was doing this. He carried Jozef's violin-case and the bundle.

" Our home is there," he said, which did not seem a very satisfactory reply.

So we four men, two boys and sixteen sheep proceeded towards the river. It ran far below the level of that field and in the shelter of those lofty banks were shrubs of great luxuriance and even trees. The shepherd-boy was pointing out to us his father's house, a long, low wooden building scarcely visible amid the vegetation.

He who had been so suspicious when I questioned him about his home suggested now that I should enter it. His mother would be there, he said. So while the rest of them went to the river he conducted me across a shaky bridge and down a narrow lane whose slipperiness made it as much of an ordeal as the bridge.

But we had been observed by the boy's mother. She came out onto the threshold and I felt that if the hazards of the journey had been multiplied a hundred-fold it would have been worth while.

CHAPTER IX

Presumably her life was hard. And yet with her dark eyes, her flaxen hair she looked as if she were the elder sister of the curly-headed boy. But how did she retain this youthfulness? While I was wondering she held out her two arms in welcome; they were bare up to the elbow. It was noticeable how the hands were rough.

"I have been waiting for you," she announced, "through several days. You are the answer to my prayer."

Most men, I think, would lose their balance if they heard themselves addressed in such a fashion. Many of them would have something like a mist before their eyes. But it was possible for me—though ninety-nine times in a hundred I might not have had this power—to keep myself comparatively calm. Thus I could see that it was not her youthfulness alone which was surprising, but the incongruity of her in this environment. Her dress was of a blue and cheap material, and she ennobled it. Everything about her was delicious, with the sole exception of her hands.

"What is it," she was saying, "that you want to ask me?"

"Pardon me," I said, "but have you always lived here?"

" Where else should I live ? There is an aunt of
mine, she helps us. Otherwise we are alone."

" You and your husband and . . ."

" Oh no," she said, " for he went to America." She
did not seem to think it strange. " And now," she
said, " let us go in."

I followed her. One stepped immediately into the
living-room, a crowded place, for in the centre of it
was a table which had evidently been intended for a
bigger room, and on the other side of it there was a
cow which an old lady was just milking. Both of them,
the cow and the old lady, turned at us their stupid,
faithful eyes.

Upon the table there were a variety of objects—a
sewing-machine and a vase of yellow flowers and some
grasses from the river-bank, and several plates with
the remainder of a meal and a slab of highly scented
soap and the photograph of a man with projecting ears, and some linen that was going to be
washed.

But I was waiting for an opportunity to ask about
the migrant husband. Maybe that he was too poor
to take the whole family ; but, I thought, it must be
dreadful for him to remember that his exquisite young
wife was in this lonely place.

" I suppose," I said, " that everyone is good in this
part of the country. Now that I think of it, I have not
seen a prison for a long time."

" Well," said my hostess, " they are good enough.

Will you please take off your bag ? How can one travel with such quantities of luggage ? "

I informed her that the articles her son had put down on the floor belonged to someone else and that he, with two others, had gone fishing.

" You should hear him play ! " exclaimed the lad. " I brought this gentleman so that his friend would come." The boy was very proud of his successful strategy.

And I, in order to survive his treatment of me, let my thoughts dwell on his mother's words : she had been waiting several days for me, I was the answer to her prayers.

Meanwhile she pulled my heavy bag along the floor and towards another room. When she returned she said that they had only got potatoes in the house, because they were quite poor. But if my friend would catch a fish. . . .

I should have said that we would not inflict ourselves upon her. But I was incapable of saying it.

She urged me to sit down and, as I happened to be opposite the dirty linen, I drew back my chair a little distance.

As she brought her own chair round she smiled and she sat down beside me, very close beside me. She was evidently one of those whom they call Nature's children.

" I am so pleased that you have come," she said, what time she laid a hand on mine.

" With regard to that," said I, " you mentioned that you have been waiting for me. Have you waited very long ? "

" Nine days," she said without a moment's hesitation. " But it will be better if I tell you everything." She closed her eyes and frowned, I know not why, because she did not seem to have the slightest trouble with her memory.

She had omitted to remove her hand, but I was perfectly content to let it stay there. I was also glad that I had chosen just that spot, for now I was receiving a bouquet of odours that were blending satisfactorily with one another. If the dirty linen had been flavoured, as it were, with the remains of garlic on those plates I do not think the product would have been delightful. But the potent perfume of the yellow flowers and the scented slab of soap each fitted admirably into the whole scheme.

" When my husband went away," she said, " and left me with our little son . . ."

" The other lad is not yours ? "

" No," she said, " but he is a good boy. My husband sailed off to America and we . . . we went on living here."

" Yes," said the woman of the cow, " that is quite true."

" I do not find fault with my husband," said the younger woman, " because he went to America, but because he sends me no money. I was looking at his

photograph the other day and I resolved to wait no
longer."

" You are going," I said, " to join him ? "

" When I have no money ! "

" Oh, you will go down to Kubin or some other
place. Up here," I said, " it may become monotonous."

" Where would you have me go to ? " asked my
hostess. The poor little thing looked so pathetic.
She was leaning towards me, but the aunt, while one
could hear the squirts of milk methodically fall, was
contemplating us across the table.

" You might go," I said, " to Kubin. If you could
exchange this farm for . . ."

" But," she interrupted me, " what is the use of
going there or anywhere ? I tell you I have got no
money. That is because my husband has found another
woman in America. But I have prayed to the Blessed
Virgin—I am a religious woman—I have prayed and
asked her for a man, so that I could revenge myself."

It seemed to me as if the blood was shouting through
my head—that and the clangor of the milk were the
two noises which drowned all the rest. They vied
with one another—they fell crashing, wave on wave,
against the rocks that were as cruel as themselves.
They screamed in horrible, fantastic mirth.

When I, at last, could dare to look at the two women
they displayed no sign of perturbation. As it chanced,
the boy had left the room, but I believe that if he had

been present this would not have modified his mother's observations.

" Thank you very much," she said. " I see you sympathise with me, that you are trying to find out a way. What can I do ? What can I do ? "

The dear thing was so troubled that I would have given much to soothe her. She was on the verge of tears.

" Let us be calm," I said, " and think it over."

" That," said she, " is just exactly what I told myself nine days ago. I settled to be calm. You see, I had been looking at his photograph, that photograph there on the table. Is it not a wicked face ? "

" Well," I said, " well . . ."

" It is wicked. He has taken the other woman. He actually had the heart to write me that. But there is one thing that is good ; he has not put on me a girdle of chastity. You know what they used to put on their wives in the Middle Ages before they started off on a Crusade."

" If he had done that . . . but," I said, " I suppose it is not the custom to have a duplicate key ? "

She gazed at me. Her eyes were infinitely sad. " We should have met each other years ago," she moaned.

Was it impossible to solace her ? I said that even if we had encountered one another years ago and if we had become quite friendly and if I had thought— which is not certain—of the duplicate, perhaps she would have answered me that it was too deceitful.

She burst out into a shrill and bitter laugh. "Against a man like that!" she cried. "And I am not to be deceitful!"

"My dear friend," I said to her, "we settled to be calm. What was it you resolved upon nine days ago?"

"Yes, to be sure. It was that when the first man came here I would ask him to help me."

"Your husband," I began, "is certainly to blame."

She clapped her hands. "He is!" so she exclaimed. "It is a grand idea! My life would have been ruined. Now . . ." she flung her arms around me and ecstatically pressed me to her bosom. "You and I!" she sang. "Oh, you and I!"

This did not seem to disconcert the aunt or the good cow. They, both of them, turned placid eyes upon us. Then the aunt said that her work was finished; would I like to have a cup of milk?

"Oh, drink it, drink it!" begged the niece. "I wish that I could give you some rare wine because of that idea."

"But if your husband should return?" I said.

"He is as stupid as a carp. It serves him right."

"He would have been less stupid," I agreed, "if he had told you nothing of the other woman."

"A man who does things like that," she said severely, "he is one who must expect to lose all kinds of things. It shows you what sort of a man he is. And, while he behaves like that, he thinks I will behave myself with every care. It would be most unjust. He takes another woman and I . . . come in, come in ! I say."

It was the director. As he was not fishing he had found it dull, he told us, by the river.

" There is only one way," said the aunt, " which is not dull and that is when they fish with dynamite. The roadmakers . . ."

" It would," he interrupted, " have been better if they had attended to the road."

" That was a long time back," said the old woman, " but I well remember we had fish in plenty. Since then I have sat occasionally by the river, thinking of those happy days."

" You are a reprobate," said the director, " but perhaps your life has been too busy for you to go fishing."

As she answered him she stroked the cow. " Yes, you are right," quoth she, " I am too busy to resemble some of you and pull the fish out one by one, or like some others who pull out no fish at all."

We spoke of miscellaneous matters for a time, such as the possibility of buying land appropriated (with due compensation) from the Church, since there was now a law for everyone which only authorizes them to hold a certain area.

" Our Party, the Monsignor's Party," said the director, " is against that kind of appropriation from the Church."

" But if it is taken from all others, for what reason," I asked, " should it not be taken from the Church ? "

" We are against it," said the director. " As for you," he said to our beautiful hostess, " I hope that if your husband has some Church lands offered him he will decline to buy them. What we always say is this : that if you take Church lands you will be cursed in the Hereafter."

" But we would have the land in this life," she replied, " and there is time enough to think of the Hereafter."

" My young woman, you are sacrilegious," he retorted.

She leaned forward, with her elbows on the table. " You may think," she said, " that we know nothing of the land, because we have so little. But I will tell you. Do you know Mr. Labanský, he who does not care what he says, so that everybody loves him ? "

" You mean Dr. Labanský, the Catholic priest ? Of course I know him."

" I want to tell you. A gentleman came here from the Land Office."

" Is he the one who offered you some Church lands ? "

" I want to tell you about something else. He said that the famous Labanský presented himself at the Land Office and asked for a farm to be allotted to a very patriotic Slovak. The Land Office remarked that the district of that farm is quite Hungarian and was he not afraid that they would influence his friend ? ' What ! ' cried the priest. ' Shall the blood of Labanský become Hungarian ? ' ' I fail to understand you,' said the gentleman of the Land Office. ' He has married,' said Labanský, ' he has married one of my daughters.' "

" What is the smell ? " ejaculated the director, with his features drawn.

" How you change the subject ! " jeered our hostess.

" Not at all," said he.

Then, by the grace of memory, I could proceed to her assistance. I related how a certain woman lay in bed, and how the husband rolled, half drunk, into the room. She thereupon reviled him, pointing out that she had all the household cares, that she bought everything the children needed, that she sent them punctually to school and doctored them if they were ill, that everything connected with the servants and the food, that everything in fact was done by her and that he was the worst of husbands, absolutely of no value whatsoever and that now he was half drunk. " Who is that fellow," asked the husband, " who is lying there in bed with you ? " The wife was furious. " Of course," she cried, " of course you change the subject."

For this help which I had given her I was rewarded with a radiant smile.

" You must excuse me," the director said, " but really there is an unpleasant smell. What with the cow. . . ."

" Why don't you go to America ? " exclaimed the woman. " In that country, so my husband writes, they wash the cows. Yes, there they wash them."

" I am sorry to find fault," said the director, " but, really, what with the cow and the dirty linen and the other things, to say nothing of all of us—would you mind if I open a window ? "

" They are not made to open," she said. " One can see that you have never been here in the winter time. But I will open the door."

She stood there for a little time. Ah, what a picture, with the background of a sky of lapis lazuli. And then the net-work of her lovely hair tried to prevent the sun from slipping through it. And although the sky grew darker and, at last, the sun was gathered in, we had a miracle before us—now the isolated strands of hair were not aflame, but the gold mass of it was turned into a brilliant halo.

Then, with a delicious gesture, she put up a hand to shield her eyes.

" Who is it ? " asked the older woman.

She did not reply. Her face was eloquent.

" This is indeed an evening," the aunt observed. " How will it end ? Who knows what will occur ? " As a precaution she began to cross herself.

We heard the rolling voice of Hlinka. He was very jovial. When he appeared he held his hand out to be kissed by the young woman, but she did not notice his intention and he laughed it off.

" My blessing on this house," he said, as he strode in. His handsome face was flushed. He said they had been quite successful ; he had caught one fish, a trout not very large but still a good one ; Jozef had caught half-a-dozen.

He came in and after him came Jozef with the shepherd-boy draped, as it were, around him.

" We have not much time," announced the Monsignor. " I have to be at Ružomberok for a service and then a procession through the streets with torches —it will be a beautiful procession. After that we have a meeting of the Hlinka Party. He who follows Hlinka is a good Slovak, he who is seduced into another Party is a bad one."

" And," I said, " the provincial elections. . . ." I had heard that one hundred and sixty thousand voters had transferred themselves from the Hlinka Party.

" Alas, they know not what they do," said he. " I must be more active than heretofore. I must not leave unvisited a Slovak town or village, not a farmstead. Everywhere I shall explain to them—you women, for example, do you follow me ? I trust that both of you are patriotic Slovak women. Would you like "—his voice was trembling with emotion—" would you like to be Hungarians again ? Those are the people who at Szeged made me spend no less than four years of my life in prison. Thus I lost four years of life."

Just at that moment the director was examining his watch, which as the room was very dark, he was compelled to hold up near his eyes.

" Yes, yes, I know," said Hlinka, " but when one has

lost four years a few more minutes do not matter. Think of it, my friends,"—he struck a most impressive attitude—" we were subordinates, second-class citizens, in our own country. But we have good reason to rejoice. That miserable period is over, it is buried in the past. It is. . . ." He raised his arm and, with the grey locks floating round his head, the Monsignor was every inch a prophet.

" Shall we go now ? " the director was suggesting.

His Reverence gazed awhile at him, as if he did not understand. Then suddenly he shivered.

" Do you want to leave the fish ? " asked the director.

Hlinka turned to all the rest of us. His smile was even as the *Nunc dimittis* and he said that he was fortunate indeed to have so business-like a colleague. " It is true," he said, " that our tile-works are at a standstill."

" That is not my fault," said the director.

" It is not your fault. But now we certainly must go to Ružomberok and delay no more."

" I beg your pardon," said Jozef, " but I must remain here till to-morrow. The poor boy has so seldom an opportunity of hearing any music."

" But how good you are ! " declared the boy's mother.

" It will give as much happiness to me," said Jozef, " as to him."

The Monsignor took the trout from his basket.

" Illustrious sir," said the aunt, " we had heard of
you. We live removed from other people, but we
are not ignorant. I tell you, we had heard of you,
but of your kindliness, if you will excuse me, we had
not heard."

" Ah," said the Monsignor, " if only you belonged to
the Hlinka Party."

" But we will do," she said, thus answering also for
her niece. " We belong to four other Parties—there
is an abundance of them nowadays—and so, from to-
day onwards, we will belong to your Party likewise."

Then our hostess, who was standing by the table,
put her two hands solemnly upon her bosom. " I do
swear," she said, " that we will be henceforward . . ."

" But, my dear woman," interrupted Hlinka, " have
you no political sense ? How can anyone be a member
of more than one Party ? "

" With yours," said the aunt—she was evidently
pleased with her new acquisition—" with yours we
have five."

The director had taken his colleague by the arm and
was gently propelling him to the open door.

" Good-bye," said Hlinka, " good-bye. But when
you two come in to Ružomberok, ask for me. They
will tell you if I am in the church or at the bank or at
the printing-office or in the hotel. I think it is one of
the best hotels in the world."

" I hope so," I said. " A few weeks ago, before
I started on this walk with Jozef, I was somewhere in

Slovakia in a hotel that was very nice, I daresay, about three hundred years ago. But otherwise the town was delightful, and now they are building an excellent hotel."

After Hlinka and his friend had gone we set about the cooking of the fish. This was achieved by our joint labours, which reminded me of Elemér Ballog, the Hungarian Bishop in Western Slovakia, a Calvinist gentleman whom I intended to visit at Bratislava, for I was the possessor of an enjoyable pamphlet which he had written. His lordship's work among the Calvinist Hungarians caused him to spend some years, I think it was, in the United States, so that he found himself no longer limited to his Hungarian language. No, he could address himself to that vast world which makes use of the English tongue (and its derivatives). This gentleman has such a way with him that I resolved that nothing less than a wild horse should drag me from Slovakia till we had met.

While the worthy aunt cleared a space on the table and began to split open the fish, I bethought me of that paragraph in the Bishop's pamphlet where he mentions the Communists of Moravia who sought refuge in Hungary and were described by a German traveller of the eighteenth century as a people who " lived in peace and plenty, working hard, honestly and cleverly."

Jozef and the boy were building up the fire and our beautiful hostess was wiping the plates. For this purpose she selected one of the available pieces of linen and I have no doubt she chose the cleanest one. As she and her companions went about their labours they seemed very happy and they uttered no words of great moment. My thoughts occupied themselves again with the perambulating German and with his impression that " these Communists who lived manufacturing steel and ceramic objects were peaceful folk."

But when we sat down, ultimately, to consume the fish we still continued to be peaceful folk, whereas it is related of the Communists that they " had no other case for the quarrel amongst themselves than only at dinner time when dumplings were served to them, but the dumplings (Knödel) had different sizes and could not be distributed equally in a righteous Christian way."

Not only were we very peaceful, but I was at peace with everyone. They say that if you really would enjoy what you are eating you must have pursued and captured it ; but Jozef cannot have enjoyed the fish more thoroughly than I did.

There was the dear woman of the house beside me. Every movement that she made was graceful—and that adjective recalled another passage in the Bishop's pamphlet, when he talks about the sympathy of the Hungarians with the evangelical Czechs who, after the disastrous battle of the White Mountain, were driven by the Habsburgs from their homes. But the Hungarians consoled them with a book, published at Gyulafehérvar in Transylvania, whose title, says our friend the

Bishop, was : " The Consolation of the Wittenburg University, sent for the Czechs and Moravians exiled because of their religion which in this book is translated into the Hungarian language for the edification of the Hungarian Nation by the court preacher of the graceful Prince of Transylvania, George Rákóczi I."

We had little else to eat, save some indifferent bread, some coffee and potatoes. I have in my time had sumptuous repasts, but none of them remains, as this one does, within my memory. We had no wine nor spirits, yet before the meal was done I felt so charmingly exhilarated, as if I was walking on the air. I longed to walk.

A similar desire was in Pavlina. And we left her aunt and boy to listen to the violin.

How dark it was, at first. She put a hand against my elbow. " Come with me," she said, " and then you will not go astray."

There should have been a moon, but what we saw was when occasionally it could peep out through a little window, as it fled along the gloomy corridors.

" Now we are going to the river," I remarked. " One hears it very well."

She told me that she knew of a good place upon the bank. And very skilfully she led me to it, where the grass was most luxuriant. It curled about our ankles and invited us to stop.

" Here," said Pavlina, " is the place."

Just then the trembling waters glittered for a

moment.   But as we sank down into that grass we were surrounded by the sombre trappings of the night. Though sombre they were full of tenderness.

" Do you remember," asked Pavlina, " what you said about that girdle of chastity ? "

" Yes," I replied ;   " but since you are not wearing one. . . ."

" I am not wearing one," she said.

CHAPTER X

NOTHING, in fact, can have been more benevolent than the attitude taken up by the mediaeval Hungarians with regard to the persecuted Slavs. And it is a great pity that the modern Hungarians decided that they would themselves go in for persecution.

" Of course, as things have turned out," said Janč... the mayor of Ružomberok—we were sitting, after luncheon, in his very comfortable flat—" as things have turned out," he said, " one pities the Hungarians, because their strenuous endeavours were too late and they certainly tried very hard."

" After being so benevolent." I said, " in the Middle Ages."

" But, as they considered it," he smiled, " that was the attitude they always showed. You see, in their eyes it is the most enviable thing on earth to be Hungarian and they were trying to convert into Hungarians all the other people in the realm, the Slovaks and the Yugoslavs and the Roumanians. A few more years of it and they would have succeeded. As it was they turned the Slovaks—nearly all of them—away from their kinsmen the Czechs. Hungarian gendarmes did their utmost to keep the Czechs out of Slovakia. And I saw the result when I was working for the common cause in Russia during the great War. We founded, as you may have heard, the Czechoslovak Legions, who were . . . ."

" I have written rather a big book," I murmured, " about them."

" Is that so ? I am sorry. I mean I . . ."

" My dear fellow," I said, " you helped to found them and that was much more important. What were you going to say about them ? "

" Don't you think that it is sometimes very good to put the cart before the horse ? We had an army when the State did not exist. No doubt the Allies helped us with the State because we had an army. Yes, I want to tell you how we founded it among our people who were colonists in Russia and all those who managed to cross over from the Austro-Hungarian army."

I noticed on the wall a photograph of the revered Masaryk with a most flattering inscription, to the effect that Janček had done excellent service in Russia and America.

" You worked in both countries," I asked, " with Masaryk ? "

" Yes, and in Russia it was more difficult. So many of our Slovaks hesitated. They had sworn the oath of fidelity, they said, to the Emperor and King. As if the liberation of one's people were not the most sacred task."

" You were risking everything yourself ? You burned your ships behind you ? "

Jančke's face relaxed into its usual joviality. " They helped me, the Hungarians helped me with the burning," he replied. " My business happened to be a match factory. What a glare it must have made ! . . . But the Slovaks in Russia, after a time they threw off their reluctance and joined the Legions. They remembered, thank God, that they were Slavs."

I was talking politics with assiduity in order not to let my thoughts dwell on a grave disaster that was imminent : my comrade Jozef said that he would stay at Ružomberok. Some day, he had said with truth, we had to part. We were such friends, he said, that if we stayed together any longer, then the parting would be still more difficult.

We had inquired for Hlinka at the Culture House, but he had gone away to make some speeches. He had not by any means forgotten us. The bedrooms were prepared and each of them contained a letter, for the Monsignor had found on reaching Ružomberok, that his band required a violinist. If we two did not object to separating, then he would be glad to offer Jozef a position. And while Jozef went to interview the leader of the band I started off to see the mayor. This gentleman, though it was only 12 o'clock, was in the middle of his lunch. A napkin hid from me his waistcoat when he let me in. And he would not allow me to depart, especially as they had a supply, he said, of Zipser sausages.

" The Zips," he told me, as he took my arm and

marched me off to where his wife was seated in a kind of lounge, " the people of the Zips were German emigrants who came into the district long ago. It is not very far from here. In fact the bishop is the bishop of this diocese."

I told the mayor that I had met the celebrated Hlinka.

" We are on good terms," said he. (It was my impression that to be on other terms with such a man as Janček would be scarcely possible.) " The bishop of the Zips is one of Hlinka's pupils and when he came from the church where he was consecrated Hlinka stooped and kissed his hand in token of submission. After that the bishop kissed the hand of his old master. You should go up to the Zips. There are some ancient German towns, at least they were once German, full of picturesque town-halls and splendid churches. For example at Levoča there is one which has so many altars that one gets confused, but I know that the high altar, a multitude of Gothic saints in front of a fine background, is the largest wooden altar of the Middle Ages. What the museums in America and England have offered for it ! Then Kežmarok has got a wooden church, built for the Lutherans with the assistance of a Swedish king, who sent his workmen. It is like the bowels of a ship and now it is quite derelict. Beside it is the Lutherans' new church and that is probably unique. The architect intended it to be a synagogue, as one can see from the windows. But the Protestants bought it and enlarged it, so that the acoustics are all wrong and very few of the congregation can hear anything."

I thanked my host for these interesting details, which rendered it unnecessary for me to go to the Zips. Moreover, while he talked, he was regaling me with the sausages. They are among the aristocrats of the sausage world, so slenderly constructed and so delicately flavoured. One does not take a knife and fork to them, for then a great part of the juice would run away. The proper method is to dip the sausage in the horse-radish and, having bitten off a certain length, to dip again.

" You have been so instructive," I said, " about the Zips that I feel as if I had been there. And, after all, we spend our dearest moments in the towns and villages and forests that our eyes have never seen."

Janček, mayor of Ružomberok, then withdrew, like some austere old saint, for meditation, which he did by issuing a cloud of smoke from his cigar. As it dispersed he looked at me, but said no more than " H'm," since he preferred not to commit himself.

" There used to be an aged governess," I said, " who did not have an opportunity to travel. She had half a dozen Baedekers and every place in France or Italy or Germany—that is if it was large enough to have a map—was intimately known to her. I well remember, when we had been talking about Nantes cathedral, that I alluded to the house of Carrier, that monster of the Revolution. 'Coming out of the cathedral, which way does one go?' I asked. She quickly looked from right to left before she answered, as one has to be so careful of the traffic."

" Good, good," murmured Jančck. " So you think that you can leave the Zips unvisited? "

" I have to make for Bratislava."

" Then let me, although I am a business-man and not a . . a . . . I am a business-man, let me tell you a little more about the Zips. A friend of mine, Devečka, head of the Commercial School of Kežmarok—he used to be a Lutheran clergyman—is one of the most patriotic Slovaks. He can see our faults—we are too much like the Russians with their everlasting ' Nichevo' or, as the Arabs say: ' It is written.' And because Devečka sometimes tells the Slovaks of their faults they sometimes fail to appreciate him. He is going to be promoted to Bratislava and there is a young schoolmaster down there who is treated on an equality with his Czech colleagues, though he is not fully qualified. He has been told that if he will pass a certain examination—not an impossible one—he will succeed Devečka. But, instead of grasping the golden opportunity—a well-paid post, considerable influence and a very pleasant set of rooms—he will not stand for the examination. He prefers to spend his time in Bratislava cafés, talking politics. Well, I am not astonished that it makes you sad."

I told him that my thoughts had turned to something else, that I had lost my fellow-traveller. We had been walking, not for very long, but . . .

" I can help you," said Janč-ek.

" What do you mean ? " I asked.

" In this town—as you have noticed, it is not a large one—we can show another man who lost his fellow-traveller, his wife. You will admit that it is worse to lose your wife."

" But I don't see," I said, " how that is to assist me. Do you want me to think myself lucky because I have had a smaller loss ? "

The mayor stood up. " It will be best," he said, " if we go straightway and call on him. I didn't tell you that he lost his wife because she ran away with someone else."

There did not seem to be much object in this visit and I knew already that it would not keep me from remembering my sorrow.

" Come," said Janč-ek, " let us go."

The man had been so amiable that I had to humour him. Besides he surely would have sooner stayed at home. It was for my sake that he had embarked upon this expedition.

It did not turn out to be a distant one. Within three minutes we had reached the house. It was a little grocer's shop, whose door was locked because it was the mid-day interval. But Janč-ek's knuckles only had to dance a trifle on the door and it was opened.

" Oh, good afternoon, Tobias," said the mayor. " I have brought somebody to see you."

I was shaking hands with a stern kind of grocer. Such, at any rate, was what he seemed with his thin lips and rather rigid bearing.

" I am glad to see you," said Tobias.

" We are interrupting you, I fear," said Janček, " but this gentleman . . . may we go in ? "

He led the way, I followed and the grocer stayed behind, to lock the door. Behind the shop we came into the living-room, a stuffy little place. And even if the mayor had not drawn my attention to it, I would have remarked the special feature of this room. One corner dominated all the rest, for it was occupied by a big wooden saint, so big, in fact, that he would have been much more suitable in a cathedral. And in a cathedral he would have been pleasing, possibly, if he had been removed from close inspection, seeing that the modern carpenter and painter who produced him were more pious than artistic.

I regretted that my host had brought me from his comfortable home to see so dire an object.

As we sat down, he and I, upon the horse-hair sofa, he informed Tobias that it was the saint whom we had come to see.

" Thank you," said Tobias. He sat down between us and the statue on a rough sort of a chair. And lovely lines of happiness were flowering upon his face.

" When your wife," said Janček, " had deserted you . . ."

The radiant grocer nodded. " But before we talk of that," he said, " will you not have . . . what can I offer you ? Some biscuits or some Carlsbad plums ? "

I am not one of those who can resist a Carlsbad plum.

" Well now," said Janček, " will you tell this gentleman about your saint ? "

" With all the pleasure in the world." And as he turned to me he said he was the patron saint of husbands who had been deceived. " Before that, I confess," he said, " I had not heard of him. I am not so religious."

" Tell us all about the saint," commanded Janček.

" How I love him ! " said Tobias. From the way in which he glanced up at the painted effigy there was no doubt of his devotion.

" As for me," said Janček, " I acknowledge that I am not even sure about his name."

" Gengoul, Gengou, Gengoux, Gigou, Genf, Gandoul, Gingolph, Gangulphus and, in German, Golf," recited the adherent. " I have studied him and with great love. He came of an illustrious Burgundian house; his infancy was passed in perfect innocence. He fled from libertines and from the sight of anything which might impair his chastity. No indiscreet words and not even any useless ones were ever known to pass his lips."

" I do not want to say a word against your saint,"

said Jančck, " but he does not sound romantic. He should have been very careful whom he married."

" Not at all," replied the grocer. " He left everything to God. When the young man's parents died and he was very rich he took as wife a woman who was vain and worldly. God permitted this so as to test the virtues of his servant and to purify him by affliction. Gengoul went off to the wars . . ."

" Excuse me," said the mayor, " for interrupting you. But I daresay that he had to do that as a nobleman. You see," he said, " I was reading the other day the report of a lecture by our friend Seton-Watson, who is never unjust if he can help it. He was saying that in Hungary the Middle Ages lasted until 1848 ; before that the nobles did not pay any taxes, as that was a privilege reserved for all the other people. But the army was provided by the nobles, each of them so many warriors. I am certain Seton-Watson would have mentioned that if he had thought of it."

The courteous grocer waited for a moment and he asked us then if we desired him to continue. Gengoul took his part, he said, in the campaigns of King Pepin the Short. The King esteemed him for his prowess and his saintly character, so that he used to sleep in Pepin's tent. One night, when they were both in bed, the lamp began to burn again. The King got up and put it out ; and this he had to do three times before the tent remained in darkness. Pepin knew that this phenomenon would not have happened if a

holy man had not been in the tent. " Another beautiful affair," the grocer said, " which has been handed
down to us regarding Gengoul is about a journey to
his home in search of rest. He had a meal one day
beside a fountain and it was so pretty that he bought
it. God decided that the avaricious man who sold it
him should have a punishment because the man
imagined that the fountain could not be transported
and that the strange traveller was nothing but an
imbecile. So when Gengoul arrived at his own home
he struck the ground and lo ! there leaped from it the
fountain he had purchased and of course it vanished
from the other place."

The mayor was looking at his watch. " How did
Gengoul become a patron-saint ? " he asked.

" His wife was utterly unfaithful. First of all he
was perplexed. What should he do ? Then he was
with her one day near that fountain and he told her
of the rumours which were circulating. ' The most
precious gem a woman can possess,' he said, ' is her
unsullied honour. She ought to do everything to
keep it or recover it.' But Gengoul's wife was im-
pudent ; she told him that the rumours, one and all,
were calumnies. Then he invited her to plunge her
arm into the fountain ; if she spoke the truth she would
have no hurt at all. However, when she drew her arm
out she was in a fearful agony. The skin peeled off,
down to the fingers, and it hung like—like a bat's wing.
' Now I could deliver you to the severity,' said Gen-

goul, ' of the law, but I will let you expiate your fault
in penitence and tears. The dower-house shall be
your home.' He went to Avallon, where he possessed
another castle."

" I suppose," said Janček, " she declined to mend her
ways ? "

" That is so," said the grocer. " She was not the
sort of woman to be married to a saint."

" How many women are? " asked Janček.

" He sent exhortations to her," quoth Tobias. " But
she was not satisfied to live in shame. She dreaded
that he would leave all his money to the poor and she
resolved to have him murdered."

Janček lifted up his hand, to show that he desired
to ask a question. " Did she know," he asked, " if he
had made his will ? "

" I am not sure," the grocer said.

" She may have fallen into her own ambush," said
the mayor.

Tobias looked important. " When the body of the
saint was taken to Varennes," he said, " by Villetrude
and Villegose, his aunts, with hymns and torches nearly
all the way, more than one miracle was wrought. Thus
did Gengoul make it very clear that he had reached the
country of eternal bliss."

" And I had never heard of him," said Janček.

" If my wife had not deserted me "—Tobias was
extremely solemn—" I would not have known a word
about him. The celebrated Hroswitha composed a

Latin poem which is curious, they say, and which is on the passion of St. Gengoul. But I have not seen it."

Having uttered these last words, the grocer, looking very blissful, sat there with his two hands neatly folded in each other.

" We are much obliged to you," said Janček, as he got up from the sofa, " very much obliged."

" Oh, please . . ." Tobias said. " It is my greatest happiness if I can spread the cult of Gengoul. I am certain that this gentleman will bless the day, for the deep solace that one finds in Gengoul is unique. I welcome him "—the grocer held his hand out in a manner that was gallant and yet rather awkward— " yes, I welcome him into the ranks of the Gengoulians, of all the happy husbands who have been deceived."

We bade the man farewell and when we had emerged into the street and I had thanked the mayor for all his trouble he was obviously wrapped in thought.

" It seems to me," he said, when we had walked awhile, " it seems to me that your two cases are not parallel. But then," he meditated, " do you think that anyone is ever in the same position as another person ? Who is that man ? "

It was Jozef, almost dancing down the street.

CHAPTER XI

" WHAT do you think ? " he cried. " I have been offered my old post again. They want me there at Turčiansky. And will you come too ? " he said. " I am going, I am going back to Turčiansky." So excited was he that he could not stand still for a moment.

" You shall both go in my car," said Janček, " and I have a good mind to go with you."

" Tell me just what has occurred," I said to Jozef. " By the way, this is the mayor of Ružomberok."

" Please forgive me, sir," said Jozef. " I would like to stay in your town. But the leader of this band, he is a relative of mine and he has heard that Turčiansky wants me. A short time ago they threw me out and now they have repented."

" Or the customers demanded it," said Janček. " Well, you shall go back in style. When shall we start ? "

It was arranged that we would leave on the next morning.

" Here at Ružomberok," said the mayor, " there is not very much for you to see. One of our features, I am glad to say, cannot be seen at present. It is a large boulder in the river and when it is visible there is a famine in the land. My father only saw it once and

I have never seen it."

" Still, this portion of the country," I said, " does not seem to me very fertile. On the way from Kubin . . ."

" Oh, if you came by that route," said the mayor, " you saw the desolation. I remember talking to a farmer in the district and he told me that his land was the poorest in Slovakia, that it would not even support a partridge. Just then a partridge got up at our feet. ' There,' I said, ' there is one partridge at all events.' ' And was it not flying away ? ' said the farmer. . . . Yes, I love my Slovaks. And when the rising generation comes along, able to occupy all kinds of positions, then the agitators won't be able to say that the Czechs are running this province. Someone has to run it, and up to the end of the war we Slovaks had only some of the elementary schools. All the kindergarten, the industrial and commercial schools, the grammar schools, the teachers' training schools, the gymnasia, the girls' schools and the high schools were purely Hungarian. But I suppose you know all about that. And anyhow we need not stand here and talk. Let us go back to my house."

He said that he had something of great interest to show us, namely how it was in the last century at Košice. By chance he had obtained a book. He did not quite remember what the name was, but it was a nice, old book. When we reached his flat he soon discovered it. I saw it was a magazine of 1846. The mayor turned up an article by Emerich Henszlmann, a Hungarian by birth, who was a well-known art historian. The magazine was printed in Hungarian and German, and this article said that the German burghers lived in the main street and the Slovaks in the other streets, while the Hungarians in the town were only officials who had been sent there.

" Of course," said the mayor, " it was the same at Košice as in other of our towns. They made it Hungarian by special methods. I have not got the exact figures, but I believe that in 1880 it had twenty per cent Hungarians and sixty-seven per cent Slovaks, while in 1890 the Hungarians and the Slovaks were, both of them, forty per cent. The explanation is that persons of Slovak origin found it more profitable to call themselves Hungarian. We have a saying that the peacock is ashamed of its feet and many a Slovak was taught to be ashamed of his mother tongue."

" Well," I said, " it seems that I have become so thoroughly acquainted with Košice that I need have no scruples in not going there."

" Košice's name in Hungarian," said Jančेk, " is Kassa and that reminds me of some of the allegations as to how we treat the Hungarian language. I have heard ill-informed persons say that Czech is the only language allowed, in petitions one is not permitted to use Hungarian. You can judge how much truth there is in that when I tell you that we even answer them in Hungarian."

Jančck then informed me that a man was going to come to his office that afternoon with the demand that the town or the State should support him, the reason being that he had five children. So far Jančck had not seen the man, and if we liked, he said, we could accompany him to the town-hall.

Jozef had arranged to spend a few hours with his relative ; but I went with the mayor. We climbed the small hill on which are situated the municipal offices, Hlinka's church, a school or so, and a museum. The mayor's secretary was entertaining—if that word can be used—the parent of the five children. I do not know how long he had been in the secretary's room, but they were in the middle of a spirited altercation. The secretary, with a pen in his hand, was anxious to proceed with some writing ; but the applicant for help was highly indignant. There he stood, in front of the secretary. To emphasise his words he was thumping on the desk, and the few words which I happened to catch did not require any extraneous assistance.

As we entered the applicant glared at us. He was a tall, thin man with flashing black eyes, and hair which protruded from under his bowler hat.

" My dear sir," said Jančck, as he uncovered, " I have the honour to wish you good afternoon."

" This man," exclaimed the applicant, while he pointed at the secretary, " this man is . . . is. . . ." And he himself seemed to be unaware that he was taking off his hat.

" Now we will go into my office," said Janček.   He
opened the door to an inner room.   It was luxuriously
furnished, and in a moment the applicant found himself
enfolded in a vast armchair of tawny leather.

Janček produced a box of cigars.   " But why . . .
why ? " said the man as he took one.

" I am very sorry," said Janček, while he let himself
fall back into another such chair, " I am sorry to have
kept you waiting.   I understand you are one of our
patriots."

" Indeed,   that   is   so ! "   said   the   man.   He
endeavoured to get onto his legs, but from such a chair
it was no easy operation.

Janček waved him back.   " Do not disturb yourself,"
he counselled.   " We can have our talk in comfort.
Is it drawing, your cigar ?   They don't always smoke
very evenly.   But I must say," quoth Janček, " that
you are working it like an expert.   What else can you
do ? "

" What else can I do ? " he echoed and his brow was
marked with many furrows.

" Tell me," Janček said, " where have you left your
wife and children ? "

Then the man could sit no longer, for in that position
he would be unable to explain himself.   He struggled
to his feet and there was a wild look about him as he
said that all his family were at the station.   " I told
several people of this town," he said in a harsh voice,
" that it is scandalous."

" How long have they been there ? " asked Janček.

" It is scandalous ! " he cried. " What have they done, poor innocents ? But this is a bad, wicked world."

" Nevertheless," said the mayor, " that is no reason why they should go to another one. When did they last have something to eat ? Come," he said, " I want to know."

The applicant looked at his watch, which was a round, unwieldy one.

" And please sit down," said Janček, " for it hurts my neck to talk to you like this."

The applicant obeyed him. " You were asking me," he said, " when they had something to eat."

" You probably arrived," said Janček, " by the slow train from the west, that is to say at five-thirty-eight this morning. And ever since then—Oh, I wish I had been told of this."

" We were all sitting there very early," said the applicant, " and then the station-master's wife came in to see us. We were in the third-class waiting room. She spoke to me and my wife. She is a good woman."

" I know her well," said Janček.

" I went round the streets."

" Looking for work ? "

" I went round the streets," said the applicant, " and I did not know what would happen."

" Let us hope," said the mayor, " that your wife did

not have another child in your absence. And so they looked after you at the station ? ''

'' The soup for our dinner was very nice, and then we had potatoes and some meat.''

'' Yes, yes,'' said Janč_ek, '' it is a bad, wicked world.''

Maybe the applicant would have made a remark, but we were interrupted by the secretary who came in and gave the mayor a card.

'' Will you two pardon me,'' said Janč, '' if I see this gentleman ? It will not take more than a few minutes. Bring him in,'' he told the secretary.

And when a florid, bustling man appeared he made him known to us as Mr. Kulfan, the architect.

'' Under the Hungarians,'' said Janč, '' there was no lunatic asylum in the whole of Slovakia. Now we have more than one and there is a question of building such an institution at Ružomberok.''

Of course Mr. Kulfan, the architect, did not know anything about the applicant or me. He looked—I thought rather searchingly — at both of us, and then he pushed one of the large chairs across the room to-wards the applicant. And after Mr. Kulfan had settled down in it, he laid his hand quite gently on that of his neighbour.

'' My friend,'' he said, '' it is indeed a privilege to meet you.''

'' Did they tell you at the station ? '' asked the applicant.

" I do not have to be told," said Mr. Kulfan. " I am a man of heart. Such people understand those others who are now and then—how shall I say ?—not as the ordinary crowd."

It was quite clear he thought that Jančٔek had arranged for him to meet one of the future inmates, if not two. But as the applicant was more dishevelled than myself and also was more agitated, Mr. Kulfan regarded him as the more interesting case.

" Do you know my opinion ? " said the applicant. " I was telling it to the mayor some minutes ago."

" Pray tell it me," said Mr. Kulfan in a most soothing voice.

" It is that the town or else the State must support me. I have a wife and five children."

" But even if you had no wife at all and no child, I would answer you that you must be supported. We live in a civilized age of the world, I am glad to say, when there is not the old indifference. One does not often hear of anyone in this advanced Republic who would not agree that you must be supported."

" And that I need not do any work ? " said the applicant.

" Oh, as for that, maybe a little light work . . ."

" But I do not want to work ! " he cried and jerked his elbow viciously upon the arm of his chair.

Mr. Kulfan, in the best bed-side manner, told him that this was of very minor importance.

" And you said that nearly everyone agrees with you

and that has not been my experience," said the applicant.

"Poor fellow, it will all be changed. Thank God
you live to-day."

"I could not thank Him otherwise," said the
applicant.

"Precisely. . . . Now what were we talking about?"

"I am not sure," said the applicant, "about this
gentleman, who is the mayor of this town. I am not
sure that he agrees with you."

Throughout this duologue the mayor and I had
sat in silence. We were wondering when and how it
would conclude. So Janč'ek was drawn into it.

"Oh, surely," said Mr. Kulfan, "surely our friend
here is mistaken. You would not. . . ."

"Mistakes are in the air," said Janč'ek. "Let us
talk, if you have no objection, of one thing at a time.
You want me to urge the building of an asylum in this
town ? "

"I do, I do ! " said Mr. Kulfan. "A primitive
people does not go mad, but when you start to be
civilized then you ought to lay the foundation stone
of your asylums. And the more civilized you are the
more asylums you will need. I rejoice, for I am devoted
to my Slovaks, I rejoice to think that we have one at
Levoča and one at Košice, and I maintain that Ružomberok has the right to have one too."

"Have you got the plans with you ? " asked the
mayor.

Mr. Kulfan took some papers out of his breast-pocket, but as he was not beside a table he did not know where to lay them down. " Suppose I spread them on the floor ? " he said. " And then we all can gather round them."

" I was going to ask you to leave the plans here," said Jančck, " so that they can be studied at leisure."

" But then," objected Mr. Kulfan, " then this gentleman may not be available and I would be very glad to hear his views. He will permit me to say—for it is evident that he is only slightly stricken—he will permit me to say that this occasion is historic, if not unique. Yes, I imagine it must be unique, so that our names will be handed down to posterity." His face was radiant.

" That is very gratifying," said Jančck, " but why exactly is it so unique ? "

" I should have thought that it is obvious," said the architect. " Do you think it has ever happened before that a gentleman who is going to live in an asylum has been consulted with respect to the building scheme ? "

Then it was that the applicant leaped to his feet. " You think that I am mad ! " he cried. " How dare you think that I am mad ? " He grabbed at Mr. Kulfan's plans and, if the architect had not swiftly put them behind his back, the infuriated applicant would have seized them and torn them to pieces.

Naturally the architect was likewise very perturbed.

" If I am in the wrong," he said, " I certainly apologise. Oh, if I do not start at once, I shall be late for an appointment. Gentlemen," he bowed to us, as he was in the act of walking out, " I bid you all farewell." He stopped beside the door. " Just let me tell you this," he said, " that it is no dishonour to be mad. On the contrary. The person who is altogether sane—but fortunately there are not many of them—is unbearable." He slammed the door, as if he was accusing us of being so repellently sane.

" Do you not think," said Janč'ek, " that it will be better if we make no more allusions to this incident ? Let us continue with our little talk. You were maintaining," said he to the applicant, " that you should be supported by the . . ."

" I have changed my mind," declared the applicant.

" What do you mean by that ? "

" This man of the asylum said that it is right. Whatever he says, that I will not do. No, not if I should live for ever."

" You will do some work," said Janč'ek, " so that you can keep your wife and children ? We must find out what positions in the town or in the neighbourhood are vacant. Ho there, Mr. Secretary ! "

CHAPTER XII

JančEK's chauffeur is, in his own line, as competent as Janček. His business it was to convey us from Ružomberok to Turčiansky, and this he accomplished with not one untoward incident. We sped through the green valley in which Ružomberok stands and then across a range of hills, until the road goes winding down again, while far away you see the tower of Turčiansky's ancient church. We did not have to stop for anything, so that we made no new acquaintances. Of course one can, as one flies past a person, say at forty miles an hour, discern in him this quality or that. But the profoundest connoisseur of human nature—as we all are—may fall into error in the making of such diagnoses. For example, as that road wound upward from the Ružomberok valley we went by two road-repairers, one of whom I thought was of a rather limited intelligence, the other being sinister. If we could have discussed a point or so with these two men we might have found that what we had perceived was nothing but a veil, behind which there was lurking an Alladin's cave of other qualities. And God knows what the road-repairers thought of us as we went rushing by.

It was an open car, which rendered conversation

difficult at such a speed. But when we came in sight
of Turčiansky we two who had been there could not
keep from speculating about our old friends.

" The Serb of your hotel was good to me," said Jozef.

" I hope," I said, " that he will be less melancholy
now."

To utter even these few words required a great
exertion. Presently, however, we began again.

" I wish," said Jozef, " you would stay at my
hotel."

" But Turčiansky is so small," I said, " that we will
often meet. If I do not go back to him the Serb might
hang himself."

" Those people in your room," he smiled.

" The prefect is a kindly person and that maid," I
said, " is a great character. You should have seen
her marching with my laundry on her back. Good
Heavens ! "

Jozef and the mayor were startled.

I had recollected suddenly that she desired from
me a box of chocolates. Where could I get one now,
for in a few miles we would be in Turčiansky ? And
to buy one there would seem too much an afterthought.

When I told Jozef what the trouble was he settled
instantly that we must look in somewhere else. He
shouted at the chauffeur that we wanted, first of all,
to go to any town where they had decent shops.

" Žilina," the chauffeur shouted back.

We had to traverse part of Turčiansky, but I pulled

my hat down on my face, and so did Jozef. We could therefore hope that nobody would recognize us.

" Well, she must be beautiful, this maid of yours," said Jančck.

" She is like a very solid paper-weight," I said, " but she is joyous. I am looking forward to her more than I can tell you."

Žilina is twenty miles or so from Turčiansky and the end half of the journey is through a delicious valley, where the river, road and railway intertwine almost as much as if they were the strands of a girl's hair. The railway passes through a tunnel, while the road and the broad, limpid river swerve off to the right ; and presently, when we have turned this way and that, enchanted by the changing views, across the road and river flies a bridge, straight from the tunnel's western mouth.

It was written that we were not merely to find chocolate in the town, for just as we pulled up outside the shop a passer-by and Jančck hailed each other.

" This is Fedor Ruppeldt," said our friend.

Except that Mr. Ruppeldt had a serious and most intelligent expression there was nothing to inform us that he is a Lutheran cleric. In Slovakia these gentlemen do not habitually wear the garb of their profession. The chief article, at any rate the most striking, in Mr. Ruppeldt's dress that day was a provincial speciality, a Slovak shirt and collar of one piece. It has been said that men's attire should be such that one does not notice it ; but probably that is a latter-day pronouncement, while the Slovak shirt and collar garment, worn without a tie and fastening down the back, has great traditions. It is usually well in view, because of the low waistcoat worn outside it, and the blue and white, in resolute squares, of Mr. Ruppeldt's specimen, was very Slovak, though a stranger might have felt it to be noisy. And a person meeting Mr. Ruppeldt for the first time could not but be struck by the incongruous appearance of that shirt and of the introspective face above it.

" What is new ? " asked Janček as we disembarked. " I saw that you are building near the station. More and more hotels. Your town is prosperous."

" The timber-trade is flourishing and now we are a railway centre. It is like a lesson in geography each afternoon," said Mr. Ruppeldt, " when there are carriages with Polish, German, Austrian, Roumanian and Hungarian destinations, not to speak of those in the Republic. They are shunted to and fro—it is quite intricate."

He went with us into the shop and as the owner of it was a member of the Lutheran minority we were received in the most cordial fashion. So the buying of the chocolates took us rather a long time. Then we got back into the car and we congratulated Mr. Ruppeldt on the progress made by Žilina.

" The people are so busy," he said, as he laid his arm upon the top of the door of the car, " they are so busy that they have no time for fanaticism. A great many of my congregation have entered into mixed marriages."

" The best marriage," said Janč“, " is that between the Slovaks and the Czechs. We celebrated the tenth anniversary with a good deal of pomp, because the national idea must be encouraged in this people. But in twenty, fifty, a hundred years—then it will be seen what an excellent marriage it is. And now, my friend, we must be taking leave of you. I wonder if you are building as many houses as we are at Ružomberok."

" One of our biggest ones," said Ruppeldt, " should have been built with more prudence. You will know all about the disaster at Prague, where the unfinished house fell in and a number of workmen lost their lives."

" Yes, but have you had an accident like that ? " asked the mayor. " I have heard nothing about it. Look here, I wish you would come with us to Turčiansky."

" But I have a class, the senior class, to-day at noon," said Ruppeldt.

" You can come back in this car. Jump in. I want to ask you several things. It is so very odd," said Janč“, as we started down the street with Ruppeldt in our midst, " it really is odd how much gets left out of the newspapers. And I should have thought we have papers enough in this country."

" Don't blame them in the matter of that house," said Ruppeldt, " because it has not fallen in yet.

But after the catastrophe at Prague it is accused of being fragile and the builder is in a quandary."

Jančsek had been enveloping the clergyman in a rug.

" By the way," said Ruppeldt, " did you read that speech of the President when he was the host of several hundred children ? He alluded to that awful accident of the house and he pointed a moral from the use of inferior cement. He says what he likes."

By this time we were out in the open country. " Of course he does," said the mayor. " What about those forgeries in Bohemia, years and years ago ? It was held that they were ancient Czech writings and he stood up alone and denounced them. Everybody screamed at him for his lack of patriotism, and what did he care ? He is splendid. Don't you think you had better put that rug across your mouth ?—we are going rather quickly."

" Yes, I only want to say," said Ruppeldt, " that when the venerated man was talking to those children in the castle at Prague it was delightful when he said that perhaps a future President of the Republic was among them and, addressing himself to that small boy, he gave him some beautiful advice."

No more was said until the car slowed down in traversing a minor railway junction. Ruppeldt then observed that he was sorry Jančsek had not come the previous day. He would have met a man from Kež-marok, the head-master of the textile school.

" You can tell me about him after we arrive," said

the mayor. " These two gentlemen have friends to
see at Turčiansky."

" The school was established by the town authorities
and instruction used to be in German. It became Hungarian in 1895. Now it is Slovak and Czech, not merely
on account of the political change, but because there
is scarcely a German pupil left and the Hungarian
factory-owners decline to have any young men from
the school. Practically all the positions they get are
in Bohemia and so it is reasonable that their lessons
should be in the national language. It is what the
pupils ask for. They are to be envied—they only have
to pay (if they can afford it) fifty crowns a year and
they live at the school gratis."

" It all sounds very nice," said Janček.

" An agitator is in the town, a certain Lonza, who
used to work for Hungary. He knows very well that
it would be hopeless to try to re-introduce the Hungarian language, but he demands that the lessons
should be in German. Otherwise he says that the
school will be closed and the buildings returned to the
town authorities."

" I should like to know the legal position," said
Janček.

And curiously enough when we rolled into Turčiansky there was a lawyer, a school-friend of Janček's.
He was mopping his brow as he strode along the pave-
ment.

" Hullo ! " exclaimed Janček. " What is all this ?

Has the doctor ordered you to take exercise ? You should walk to Marienbad if you want to be slim again."

He told us that he was tramping two hours every day, one after his morning's work and one in the evening. He no longer ate potatoes and he did not drink till he had finished eating. He would like to know, he said, if Jančak thought his figure had improved.

" Oh, well, perhaps it has," said Jančak. " And there is a legal question I would like to put to you."

He could spare us a little time, he said, just then. It was therefore arranged that Jančak and I should go with him, that Ruppeldt should be driven back to Žilina and, on the way, the chauffeur should bespeak a room for me and leave my luggage and the chocolates at the Slovan. As for Jozef, he would meet us there for lunch ; but first of all he would present himself to his proprietor.

Jančak, with the lawyer on one side of him and me on the other, marched away at a good speed. " I think I ought to tell you this," he said to his old friend. " I am not bringing you a heavy case. I only want to ask you something."

" I am very glad to be of service to you," said the man of law.

When we reached the office, where another man, his partner, was at work, he drew up three chairs to the stove.

The mayor was whispering to me that we could talk

quite undisturbed ; he knew the partner. " He is one of those," said Janč003k, " who have the enormous gift of concentration." Then he told our host that it was difficult, the problem he would put before him, as it had to do with the original and, later on, the new administration of a school.

" The time will come," said the lawyer, " when the whole Republic will have, not the present Austrian code, but an improvement on it. In the meantime Slovakia has the legal practice that prevails in Hungary."

" How interesting," I said. " Do you mean that the Hungarian laws are still maintained in this country ? "

" Would you like an illustration ? " he asked. Then he looked out of the window, while he rubbed his lower lip. " But why not ? " he burst forth. " I am sure that both of you are discreet and I will not mention her name." Nevertheless he was very red in the face.

" It happened in this office," he began. " I told her if she was not certain who the father was, then let her choose that young man she had been with who himself had got the richest father. That is what we always tell them. By Hungarian law the father of the young man has to pay, which is quite just, because the son has probably no money and is working on the old man's farm."

" I never gave the matter much attention," said Janč003k, " but it seems to me that if a farmer is really rich, for example if he were to inherit from an American uncle, then half the girls of all Slovakia would swear that his son is the parent of their child. It would be very hard on that farmer."

"It would be," said the lawyer, "a kind of tax on his wealth."

"But what could he do to prevent it?"

"He could do nothing," said the lawyer, "except to lock up the son and then the son could sue him for his liberty. Do you know that our Habeas Corpus Act—not down here, of course, but in Bohemia among the Czechs—do you know that it was passed some centuries before the English one? True, it was only for the nobles and the burghers—they had to be judged within a certain time. There was no such stipulation for the serfs. But still our Habeas Corpus was much better, you will agree, than nothing. For the early fourteenth century it was a most enlightened measure."

"Very good," said Janček. "And with regard to that girl, what happened next?"

The lawyer cleared his throat. "She came to me a second time," he said, "and, as I told her, I was not surprised, for she had grown more handsome through her motherhood. A young man would have been worth nothing if he had not been in love with her. Which of the young men was the father of the second child we did not know. I recommended her, however, to assert it was the same one as before. This would give her something of the reputation of a faithful woman. And, besides, the father of this youth was so much wealthier

than all the others. . . . Two or three months later
I was in the market-place. You know the sort of
sunlight, when the oranges are balls of glowing fire—
it was a day like that. The girl was a sweet saint,
demure in loveliness. ' Is there another child,' I asked,
' on the good road ? Well, you had better come with
me,' I said, ' and tell me at my office all the news.'
And so she came. I was as serious as I could manage.
' Little girl,' I said, ' do not be altogether shameless.
By Hungarian law, if you are that, then you can get no
money on account of parentage.' ' What is it, to be
altogether shameless ? '' she inquired. ' I am not sure,'
I said. ' We women,' said the girl, ' we are unfortunate.
We try, so many of us try, to lead an honourable life,
and if we do we run the risk of being charged with
coldness. All the young men we reject will say that we
are cold. What can a poor girl do ? ' I well remember
how with my own handkerchief I wiped away the traces
of her tears. My fingers trembled, which the girl
perceived, and in another moment she was laughing in
despite of all her grief—I thought of angels peeping
through the clouds. Well, I was near enough to following the farmers' sons.''

" But going with one other man," said Janček,
" that would not have made her absolutely shameless,
I suppose ? "

" One must be careful,'' said the lawyer. " But what
you have just remarked I told her too, when she
returned a few days later for a consultation. By that

time I had discovered that I could not live without her. And what do you think she did ? ''

" Well," said the mayor, as he spread out his hands.

" No, you are wrong ! " exclaimed the lawyer. " She pretends that, if she were not virtuous with me, then she would fall into that list of women who are known as shameless. We have argued it and argued it."

" I hope," said Janček, " that you do not let your business go to ruin."

" We have made a compromise. She says that if in my appearance I am not so fat—I used to lead a sedentary life—if I can make myself less fat, she says, and more like one of the young farmers' sons, then she will treat me kindly."

CHAPTER XIII

A GREAT advantage that the stage enjoys over life is in the matter of entrances and exits. Here had I been dreaming of my friends at Turčiansky, of the melancholy Serb, the amiable porter who had taken me to the museum, and the sturdy little maid. How glad they all would be to have me back. I pictured them, collected round me in the hall, the Serb less melancholy and the porter grinning and the maid just touching me upon the arm, to make quite sure that I was safe and sound. Then all of them would ask their questions, not expecting any answer, and I gradually would be moving up the stairs, with them still fluttering round me, to the same room I had had before. Its tidiness would make me feel uneasy, but all that would be obliterated by the admirable words of my three comforters.

However when, with JančEk, I came into the Hotel Slovan, I had a very different reception. The Serb was standing behind the counter on which lay the visitors' book and he thumped the counter with such vehemence that a good part of the formidable book leaped into the air. On the opposite side of the counter was the maid and she was labouring under such excitement that not only was her face quite hot but even her arms—she

173

chanced to have the sleeves of her dress turned up to the elbows.

They did not fail to greet me as I came in, but for the moment their main business was elsewhere.

" I am so glad to see you again," said the maid. " Did you ever hear that one does not know a language if one cannot spell it ? "

" That is so ! " thundered the Serb. " It is pleasant to have you back. I hope it has gone well with you. And as for not spelling one's own language ! We had the glorious Vuk who simplified the Serbian tongue about a hundred years ago and every word of it is written as it is pronounced."

" You are lucky," said I, " but they have not had a Vuk everywhere."

" All I know is this," shouted the maid, " that one of the greatest of our Slovaks, General Dr. Štefánik, who was the son of a clergyman—and those were the boys who got the best education—did not, as a grown man, spell the words like everybody else. How could he do it, when some spell them in one way and some in another ? "

" What a language ! " exclaimed the Serb. " But you have not told me anything about your journey."

" It is a fine, fine language," declared the maid. " I heard of a policeman at Bratislava. He was Hungarian and he passed the Slovak examination, and he said he was not sure if he ought to put i or y at the end of a word. ' Don't let yourself be worried,' they

told him, ' because the Minister himself does not know.'
How should we know our language so well—I mean the
grown-up people who went to school before we had our
freedom—when twenty hours a week were given to
Hungarian lessons in the Slovak villages, where everyone was Slovak except the schoolmaster and the notary
and the doctor ? ''

" We will go on with that another time," said the
Serb. " These gentlemen are waiting."

I told him that Janček would depart after lunch.

" How I envy him," said the Serb. " Here am I
chained to a town that only has a past. But let us
go upstairs."

When we were half way to the first landing the maid,
who was a step or two in front of us, suddenly stopped
and turned round. " I do not understand," she said
to the proprietor, " why you speak like that about
Turčiansky. People live here just like in other places."

" Wait until I go away, my good woman," he said,
" and this hotel is shut up."

" But," she remarked, " I am not going to stay here
as long as that."

" Oh, are you giving me notice ? This is the first
I have heard of it."

" When this gentleman goes I am going with him.
Another woman," she explained, " will look after my
school-boy son. Jozef will stay here now and the gentleman will not like to walk alone."

" If you don't go any faster than you are going now,"

said the Serb, " he will take a long time to reach his destination. By the way," he said, "what is your destination ? "

As we went on to the second floor, I told him that I had no rigid programme.

" If I were a free man," he sighed, " that is how I would travel. I would get out at a place because it has a pretty name."

It occurred to me that if the maid was going to walk with me it would be convenient to know her name.

" But have you forgotten," she asked, " that I am called Maria ? " She looked very mournful indeed as she wiped an eye with the back of her hand.

" Maria," I said, " there were eleven thousand virgins."

" That is true," said Maria, " but I am very sad that you did not remember my name."

" We honour those eleven thousand," I said, " we honour them profoundly ; but as for remembering their names, I acknowledge that I cannot do so."

The Serb was inclined to support me. " In my Church," he said, " we have not got eleven thousand virgins and if we had I would not remember half their names."

" One of them is almost certain," I said, " to have been Maria. And I venture to say that she, being a holy woman, would pardon me for not remembering her name."

" A name is not everything," said the Serb. " We

have in our Church half-a-dozen saints who are called John. But do you think that there is no difference between, say, the holy apostle and that Saint John Rilski who was a shepherd near the Rilo Monastery and was canonized because one day he met a Turk in his path and knocked off his head ? I tell you," quoth the Serb, " that there is all the difference between the one Saint John and the other."

" How did he knock off the fellow's head ? " asked Maria.

" Oh," said the Serb, " just like that." And he swept his arm through the air as if it had been a scythe.

Maria was at the foot of the bed, allowing her bare arms to rest upon the metal work. She considered them and clearly she was ill at ease. " If," said she, " you can knock off a man's head as easily as that, how terrible it is."

" Very unpleasant," admitted the Serb, " if his blood falls on your clothes. But you become a saint."

" How often have I boxed the ears of my son," said Maria, " and to think that I might. . . ." She shuddered.

" Maria," I said, " before I went away from this place, you asked me to do something for you."

" Oh, did I ? " said she. " And one single blow and I would have had no son."

The Serb was going towards the door. " Shall we go down," he said to me, " now that you have seen your room ? And as for your son," he said to Maria,

" you must practise how to do it before you can knock off a man's head."

" Did your John Rilski," she asked, " always practise on Turks ? "

" I will be perfectly frank with you," said the Serb. " Very little is known about him. In fact nothing at all, except his one exploit."

I had been waiting for an opportunity to speak. " You asked me," I said to Maria, " to do something for you. And I did not forget. Here is the box of chocolates."

" Oh, thank you, thank you," she cried. " What a wonderful memory you have."

And thereupon, leaving Maria in this happy frame of mind, I decamped.

Janč2ek had been a silent listener during these transactions. " Well, you have some luck," he said as we went down the stairs. " It is exceptional to find a travelling-companion like Maria."

" And I hope," I said to the Serb, " that I shall not be causing you an inconvenience."

He said that, on the contrary, he had been troubled in his mind about disposing of the staff of his hotel, for he did not intend to stay for ever at Turčiansky. And now he would be relieved of one of his subordinates.

" But she will not stay with me," I cried, " for ever."

" That," he said, " is what I thought."

" Sooner or later she will come back to you."

He was extremely calm. " When she is going with

you through the land," he said, " she will have opportunities to seek another place. You will be able to
recommend her."

" It is only as a travelling-companion that I have
thought of her," said Janč<ček. " She is not an ordinary
person. But perhaps you are one of those who attract
to themselves the rare people."

Jozef was expecting us in the dining-room. So were
the waiters, who saluted me with reverent smiles. I
did not know what Jozef had been telling them or what
they imagined, but the welcome which they gave me
would have been most seemly for a scientist who had
spent thirty years among the vermin and the tempests
of Tibet.

To choose a waiter so as not to disappoint his
brethren was a task for which I felt unequal. So I
simulated great fatigue and even groaned as I sank
down into the nearest chair. Janč*ček and Jozef took
their seats beside me. Half the waiters in the room
were hovering around.

" We are very glad to have you back," remarked the
head waiter.

" And what you must have been through," said one
of his colleagues.

" It will be good," said the head waiter, " if you
have an egg in your soup."

Those waiters who had, perforce, to attend on the
other clients were having some compensation by talking about us and from every quarter of the room

we were the target of curious eyes. But this very public lunch came to an end at last and Janček said he must return to Ružomberok.

"I have an idea," said Jozef. "Let us drive a little way with him before we say good-bye."

In five minutes we were seated in the car and in ten minutes we had left the last house of Turčiansky behind us. For a time the road was fairly level, then it started to ascend and presently we had to stop, because a roadmaker's cart, which had carried a load of stones up to that point, was in the act of turning round.

There it seemed advisable for us two to get out. We bade farewell to Janček and the chauffeur. For a time we watched the car and then, as we turned round, there lay the dappled fields spread out beneath us, the small greyish town, the guardian, shadow-coloured hills, the faintly azure sky.

I felt as if it would be sacrilege to break that silence.

"Ah," said Jozef, "all this music drowns me."

In astonishment I looked at him.

"It was to talk to you," he said, "that I arranged for us to come up here. And now. . . ." He ended in a rueful smile.

"Dear friend," I said, "I thank the gods who brought us two together. But for you I would have been insensible to this great music. Now I have begun to hear it."

How serene was my companion's face ! And when he spoke there was a furtive laughter in his voice : " Those little things we talk about—poor candles in the wind."

Unconsciously we started down the hill.

" And yet," I said, " if you will tell me why you brought me here . . ."

I think he shrugged his shoulders. " We must bid farewell," he said. " I meant to vanish and say nothing."

" We have nothing to regret," I said.

" How strange, how strange it is," said Jozef.

I suggested we should rest a little by the roadside. We could make ourselves quite comfortable leaning up against a pile of stones. We went down on our knees, to hollow out two places for our backs. And when the work was done and we were sitting side by side I mentioned that I did not envy Rothschild his luxurious armchairs.

" Well, I have heard of him," said Jozef, " but I do not know what kind of chair he has."

We sat there for a while in meditation.

" Yes," he murmured, " it is strange. A week ago we did not know each other."

A green lizard was engaged in taking by assault a rock, a jagged rock of no great size, but large enough to have been left there in the field to incommode the ploughman. It was near to us. The lizard, like an emerald necklace, glided up and up.

" I wonder if he knows why he is doing it," said Jozef.

As the little creature heard his voice it stopped and twisted round its head. And I was glad to see that it apparently approved of us, for it continued at the same pace as before upon its journey.

" There is only one thing sure," said Jozef.

" Death you mean ? And that, in spite of its exertion, the green lizard will accomplish nothing ? "

" But how much more splendid if you are the lizard rather than the rock. I shall have to wander all my life," he said. " We have it in our blood. A very long time ago, when we were encamped near Rožnava in the east of Slovakia, I was spoken to one day by an old gentleman, Count Andrassý. I was a youngster— as a rule I was as happy as the day was long—on that day I was whistling gaily, I remember, till I found myself in front of the old gentleman and then I stopped. He was sitting on a bench in an avenue of trees and, a short distance away, was the mausoleum to his wife. I think it is the most wonderful mausoleum in the world ; the marbles have been brought from everywhere, the columns are like a forest and with all the shades that forests have in autumn. What it must have cost ! . . . I stood there very awkwardly. He was so full of grief and I had whistled. He did not reprove me. He had noticed me on other days, he said. Would I like to be a gardener ? "

" But everybody cannot be a gardener," I said.

" Well, that is what he offered me," said Jozef.
" If I settled down, he argued, it would be much better
for me. And I could have lessons ; he would see to that.
But then I answered him with words I did not know
were in me.   ' As the road winds round,' I said, ' it
winds itself all round my heart. How can I fix myself
in any place ?   Oh yes,' I cried, ' someday I will be
fixed, just like a leaf is blown into a corner of the
masonry of this grand mausoleum.'   And it was the
truth I spoke, because I shall be staying now at Turčiansky.   You will travel on and I will stay."

" Did that old gentleman," I asked, " try to persuade you ? "

" Yes, indeed. He went with me behind the mausoleum and he showed me where his favourite old dog
was buried, underneath a life-size monument of
terra-cotta. In its grave the dachshund has a blue
silk pillow for its head and it is wrapped up in a Persian
rug on which it used to lie."

" But how," I asked, " was that going to influence
you to be a gardener ? "   I was puzzled.

" The dachshund had stayed there for twenty years,"
said Jozef, " and I believe he meant that if I was a
vagabond I would not be buried in such pomp. . . . I
told him that I did not care about my coffin nor if I
would have a coffin. What I wanted was that they
should bury me far down, so that I should not hear
the wind. How terrible to hear the merry wind.
' Oho,' said the Count, ' so you like to listen to the

wind.' ' It blows,' I said, ' all through me.' Then the Count was nodding. ' You are right,' he said, ' you were not meant to be an ordinary citizen. Good luck to you.' "

I took up two of the small stones on which I had been sitting. As I rubbed their surfaces against each other I was working out a new idea.

" Let us arrange," I said, " to have the wind our messenger. Speak into it your thoughts when it is blowing to the west and I will answer you when it flies east again. We must not drift apart."

" So long as I am in this world," said Jozef—and he put his hands on mine—" I will be always with you. God be thanked that we have found each other."

We arose and set off towards the little town.

" Once in a summer night," said Jozef, " I was listening to a gipsy child that leaned out of the window and was talking to the moon. That night the moon ran in and out of clouds. The child was angry with it. Then at last it sailed into an open space. And unfortunately my foot set the floor a-creaking, so that the child turned round. I was afraid that I had interrupted something beautiful. ' Jozef,' he said—we were old friends—' do you think that perhaps the moon could not hear me, behind the clouds ? I do hope it didn't hear me.' "

CHAPTER XIV

Maria was immensely amused when I said that we would make for Pištany. Why a visit to a celebrated spa, where they get rid of all rheumatic ailments, should excite hilarity I did not know.

" Have you ever been there ? " I asked.

She twirled the fingers of her right hand, letting them make very much the same motion as that implement one uses for scrambling an egg. This was Maria's way of saying ' No.' Therefore she was not remembering any incident of other days.

She laughed without restraint. If we had still been in the streets—albeit they are generally broad and rather unfrequented streets—of Turčiansky, she would have excited a good deal of comment. But we had by this time left the town behind us. And we were so matutinal that the peasants were still on the way to market, some of them in painted carts and some on foot, with an opinionated pig or two in front of them, while one young man, who wore a beautiful embroidered costume, had a goodly flock of sheep and goats.

Maria marched along the road as if self-consciousness did not exist. Both men and quadrupeds regarded her and doubtless they would have been glad to know what she was laughing at.

" Oh, whatever shall I do," she cried, " whatever shall I do at Pištany ? "

" A short time ago," I said, " the thought of Pištany made you laugh and now you seem to be afraid of it."

She did not try to give an explanation. " How far is it from there," she demanded, " to Constantinople ?"

I had seen some of the advertisement pamphlets which are issued by the Pištany authorities. They contain a simplified sort of map with straight lines running from their town to some of the capitals of Europe and against each of these lines it indicates the distance in hours between Pištany and the capital in question. But, so far as I remembered, there is no line going to Constantinople.

" I should imagine," I said, " that very few Turks come to Pištany nowadays."

Her lips were parted as she turned to me and it was clear that she was suffering a bitter disappointment. " But I think you must be wrong," she said. " I think they come in swarms. Oh, I can see that you do not believe me."

" Perhaps one or two Turkish Ministers may come in the course of a season."

" But there is a picture of them. And I saw it and it was the kind of picture one does not forget. Please listen to me. First of all there was the river, very broad, and at the margin of it were the bathing-places, one with a wall of osiers round it for the women and another, just the same, for men."

" But I have also seen a picture," I said, " and it is nothing like that. There is a huge, magnificent bath-house with a dome and a whole series of other baths and long, airy corridors and a museum where people leave their crutches after they are cured. You see I have seen a picture or two."

" I have only seen one," said Maria, " and it was full of blood. The Turks were hacking at the men behind the osiers and they were seizing the women to carry them off."

Is there anyone among us who has never felt that if he had been born into some other period he would not have been misunderstood ?

I asked Maria if she really would like such events to come to pass as she had just described.

" No," she said, " I had forgotten something. If they take me to Constantinople I shall have to leave my son here in Slovakia."

" Would you prefer that we should make a detour," I suggested, " and not go near Pištany at all ? "

She did not answer me.

" Well, we have time enough," I said, " to think it over. We shall not be in that neighbourhood for several days, that is if no one offers us a lift."

" I have decided this," she said. " I will not let myself be seized, although it would be wonderful to talk about when I return. No, I refuse to let them seize me. But perhaps—now do you think that near to Pištany there are hills ? "

The pamphlet makes allusion to some hills on each side of the valley, hills with ruined castles on them. This I told Maria.

She was very glad. " Let us go up to one of them," she said, " with a good pair of glasses. We have got a proverb that the person on the bank does not get drowned."

We walked on steadily. By this time it was rather late for Turčiansky market and for a considerable stretch we had the road all to ourselves. It was a dreary kind of road.

" If you know any songs that I know," said Maria, " we could sing together."

" Have you heard," I asked, " about the Countess Bathorý ? One of those ruins on the way to Pištany belonged to her. It spoke of it in the small book I read. She was a very wicked woman."

" But those nobles ! " said Maria. " What did they not do ? A friend of mine went on a pilgrimage to Stara Hora where they have a spring and when the Blessed Virgin intercedes for you there is a miracle. My friend found that the vicar of the place had written one of those small books and therein it is said that very often in the multitude of pilgrims would be noble men and women. Do you think the Blessed Virgin cared if they were noble ? "

" Not at all," I said. " The Countess Bathorý, who

lived a few centuries ago, caused three hundred girls of the district to be slain. She thought that if she drank their blood she would have everlasting youth."

" My curse upon her ! " cried Maria. " And did she obtain her everlasting youth ? "

" They locked her up in prison. As you do not love the nobles you may like to know that they did not cut off her head because she was a member of that class."

Maria looked vindictive as she stabbed the air with her right fist. " At all events," she said, " we have not any nobles now in the Republic. It is not allowed to be a noble person. We shall have no longer any wickedness."

" A world," I said, " in which there is no murder and no rape. . . ."

" How lovely," said Maria.

" Life would be worth living then," I said.

" It would be grand," exclaimed Maria.

We tramped on till mid-day. Then—we had been talking of our lunch for half an hour—we found a shady tree to have it under. There was only one objection to that tree : some cows were under it as well. I pointed out a number of good reasons why their presence might become obnoxious. When all other reasons failed to move Maria I deployed the last, unanswerable one. But she could answer it and did so with a glittering eye :

" Two foreigners—no, it was not at Turčiansky,"

she related, " but another place amid the mountains where I also was the maid—they wanted to have, each of them, two eggs for breakfast. They did not know, nor did we at the hotel, where they would find among the mountains anything to eat. As I have told you, they were foreigners ; they did not recollect our word for ' egg.' So one of them got out a piece of paper and he drew two circles. How was I to recognize that it was eggs he wanted ? ' Come with me,' I said and then I guided him out of the house. Myself I walked all through the mud, in order that his feet should be upon the wooden planks. When foreigners go back to their own countries it is better if they say that you are high in culture."

" My good friend," I said, " you are a patriotic woman."

" So I let him walk upon the wooden planks. We came to where that room is with two circles on the door. ' Behold,' I said to him and I was proud, as well I might be. But I cannot understand those foreigners."

" What did he do ? " I asked.

Maria said that I would not believe her. Yet what she was telling me was solemn truth. " The man behaved," she said, " outrageously."

" Suppose," I then suggested, " that we have our meal. And if the cows are too unpleasant we can always move away."

Maria sat down there and then. " He laughed," she

said. " And naturally I was wrathful, after having gone myself in all the mud. ' Young man,' I said severely, ' what sort of a land is it you come from ? ' But he laughed so much he did not hear me. ' You must be out of a savage land,' I said, ' where the improvements of our age do not exist.' ' Oh, my good woman, stop ! ' he cried. The tears were running down his crimson face. And then he told me that, when he had made two circles on the piece of paper, he had wanted me to make him eggs for breakfast. By the way," she said, " I have some hard-boiled eggs for us."

The other items of our meal were cheese and bread and little strips of meat, an admirable lunch, in fact, if only there had been a stream of water, as we had no drop of any liquid with us.

Then Maria had her triumph ; as if it was one of the most ordinary things to do, she milked a cow.

The generous animal was very pleased to make her contribution to our lunch. Maybe Maria's hand possessed the needful cunning or maybe the cow was fascinated by the Slovak folk-song which was on Maria's lips.

Anyhow a rough tongue was protruded from her own lips and, despite the effort it involved, the cow deposited a trail of pure affection on Maria's hair and neck.

What with one thing and another my companion's mood was very jocund, so that while she was engaged upon the cow I broke it to her that she was too late, by several hundred years, for what the energetic Turks were wont to do at Pištany.

Her fingers were continuing their task, her mind was elsewhere.

" If you had been born in that old time," I said, " you would have made sufficient friends. But on the other hand your boy. . . ."

Fortunately it did not occur to the good woman that her husband—as to whom she never told me anything—might, with their son, have also been projected back into that earlier age.

" Oh, my dear boy, my dearest, if I could not have him," she exclaimed, " then I have no desire at all to go back to some period of history."

" There was a person," I informed her, " in my country who maintained that of all errors that which is the most gratuitous is to be a prophet. But I think that the most foolish thing a man can do is to be sad because he was not born in other days."

" And if we had been born in other days," she added, " we would now be dead. Who would not sooner be alive than dead ? "

All afternoon we trudged along. The road became so bad that we walked by the side of it. This was an empty portion of the land. The soil was very poor. No villages, not even isolated farms could be discerned until we came across a ruined shepherd's hut and, after a long hour, we reached a little farmstead

which had been abandoned. Anyhow it looked as if
that was the case ; the path diverging to it from our
wretched road was not indeed more wretched, but
there was about it something evil.

" We cannot shelter for the night in such a place as
that," I said. " We should have a roof above us probably, but . . ."

" No, no ! " cried Maria. " Let us go away."

Two dogs rushed helter-skelter from the house.
Their frightful noise was not so much the rage of dogs
as a prolonged and hopeless scream. Nor did they
rush in our direction, these emaciated dirty-coloured,
creatures, but when they had covered half the distance
from the house they sped away across the wilderness
of weed and stone.

In spite of the grim desolation that surrounded us
and that was making us draw close to one another, we
did not discuss this direful incident. We walked as
quickly as the nature of the ground permitted.

Would we find a lodging for the night ? I think we
did not care, so great was our relief to have escaped
from the mysterious dogs and their abode. We would
have been content to pass the night beneath the stars.
And it was highly probable that we would have to do
so, for the sun was far down in the shy.

Away there to our left the sun was flashing on a level
surface, which was like a mirror. Surely it must be a
pond or lake. On the far side of it were splendid trees.

" The fisherman will entertain us," said Maria.

" What if it is like that other house ? " I said.

" One does not in one day find two like that," said the consoling woman.

Then we saw that, nearly hidden in the trees, lay a considerable village. If we had possessed a map we should have known beforehand of it and have never felt the joy it gave us. This I mentioned to Maria and she nodded.

" At the same time," I remarked, "what is more fascinating than a map ? I do not know which I prefer, the maps of countries that I know or of the lands I hope to see. I could, I do, spend hours in poring over them."

" Look there ! " exclaimed Maria. " It is a big house."

More than the other houses it was difficult to see amid the vegetation, to say nothing of the twilight.

" Let us hope," she said, " that they will give us shelter."

At a little distance from the village we found that there was another road, diverging from the main one. We would have to take it if we wanted to present ourselves at the large house.

Two loiterers, their day's work done, were standing at the junction of the roads. They looked at us with interest, I thought.

" Good evening," said Maria, " you have a nice village. And what is the name of it ? "

They told us.

" We are very tired," said Maria, " we have come from Turčiansky. If we had not found your village it would have gone hard with us."

" Maybe," said one of them.

They did not appear to be communicative people.

" Can you tell us who lives in that house ? " I asked. " We hope to stay there for the night."

They glanced at one another.

" Has he got a room for guests ? " inquired Maria.

" Has he got two rooms ? " I asked.

One of the loiterers showed signs that he was going to speak. And presently he did so. " That is Kuzma's house," he said. " The man has saved and saved. I do not know how much he has in land and as for cows and geese, perhaps he does not know himself."

" There you are wrong," said his companion. " Kuzma knows all that."

" Well," said Maria briskly, " it is growing late— his wife may let the fire go out and——"

" His wife is dead," quoth the last speaker. " She died long ago—he has a cook."

" But if she lets the fire go out we shall have nothing," said Maria, " nothing hot to eat. So let us go at once."

We took our leave of the two loiterers and we met no one on that bye-road or within the precincts of the white-washed farm. We went up to the painted door-way, which was decorated with a beautiful design of birds and flowers.

13

As I was about to knock the door was opened and a youngish man appeared.

" Good evening," he said, " are you relatives of his ? "

" No," said I, " we are travellers."

" Oh," said the young man, " then you will not have heard that he is ill. I am the district doctor."

But why had those men not told us anything of this ? Our voices fell to whispers and we started to move from the door.

This did not meet the doctor's wishes. He would be obliged to us, he said, if we would go into the sick man's room. Kuzma was in a coma, but with lucid intervals and then his loneliness was terrible. We would be doing a good deed, the doctor said. He was himself just going to fetch the vicar.

We asked if Kuzma had no relatives.

" Yes, he has," said the doctor, " but he is a man of stone. I had always heard that he is the most grasping old peasant of my district. He drove his daughter away, because he wanted her to marry another rich old man and she preferred the son of a poor neighbour. I have begged him to let me send for his daughter, but he glared at me."

" The devil will take him," said Maria. " A ruffian like that . . . . ! But before he dies he must bless the daughter. It is absolutely necessary," said Maria.

She had assumed such an authoritative air that the young physician inclined himself. He undertook to send for the man's daughter.

" He will bless her on his death-bed," quoth Maria, " and after that he will die in peace."

The doctor came with us up to the threshold of the sick man's room and then he left us.

The first thing that I saw on entering the room was a long wooden receptacle hanging from the ceiling. It contained a number of loaves of rye bread, that would in this way be kept from being tampered with by mice. Two hams were suspended over the hearth ; it was one of those gorgeously decorated hearths and an array of brightly-coloured plates stood on the shelves above it. The sick man was in a painted wooden bed against the wall. His eyes were looking at us ; they were dull.

Then he became aware of us, at least of my companion who was in front of me. Remember that the last rays of the sun were streaming round her head, transmuting the loose hairs to threads of gold.

" Be merciful," he begged. His voice was very shaky. " Do not throw me out again, now that I am as far as this." He lifted a thin hand to shield his eyes. For half a minute he said nothing, but then he resumed. " Oh yes I know," he quailed, " of course they have to think it over. You archangel—will you, can I ask you to run in and give a message ? It is terrible if one is brought up here and has to wait upon the threshold."

Maria's tact was equal to this great occasion. " My poor friend," said she.

A smile passed upward from his lips and he was so exhausted that his eyelids closed.

A cat, which I had not observed before, made certain rumbling sounds ; I did not know if they were an expression of its sympathy or its own pain.

" Now that is odd," the man continued. " At the door of heaven I can hear the voice of my old cat. Well, that is very odd . . . Oh, there you are. You have come back," he said. " What did they say ? It would be awful, awful if they fling me down again."

" You must not be afraid," Maria said.

" No, no ! . . . Would it," he asked, " would it be good behaviour if I take your hand ? "

She strode up to the bedside, whereupon I moved away a foot or two from where I had been standing, so that I should not be seen. Maria he had recognized as an archangel, but he might be troubled as to my place in the hierarchy. I might have even wakened him from his delicious, enviable dream.

" What did they say ? " he whispered harshly to Maria as she placed her hand on his. " Of course they know what I have done. I have not been very charitable in my life ! "

" Do not excite yourself," she said. " We will take care of you." And then, forgetting what he thought she was, she said she wished that she had brought some brandy.

He was staring at her in amazement. " Do they have it there ? " he asked.

Perhaps her answer was a little feeble. " You will, you will see," she said.

" I have drunk brandy in my time. . . . Once I had a bottle of Tokay. Oh, what a wine ! "

She recommended him to calm himself.

" I will be calm," he said. " But if a wine is suitable for heaven, then it is that Tokay. Do they keep it there ? "

Maria said she did not know.

And he remarked that she was one of those who dealt with other things. It was the same, he said, on earth where people took an interest in this or that. " I had a happy time on earth," he said. The recollection of it made him laugh, but this was too much of a strain for his decrepit body and the laughter turned to groaning.

Presently he was so far recovered that he said he had been always very pious, which he hoped they would remember. He had gone to Mass when it was possible and he had rarely got the better of a priest and on Palm Sunday when he was a boy he used to walk in the procession. There he lay and pondered, and from that he seemed to pass into a sort of coma.

By this time the sun had vanished ; it was nearly dark inside the room. Maria had some matches with her and she lit a candle.

I peeped round the corner. It was like a Rembrandt, with the brooding darkness interrupted by that one illumination. When the man returned to consciousness he would be sure that now he had arrived in heaven.

I made signals to Maria that she should investigate, to ascertain if there was not some wine or brandy.

As she, with the candle's help, went rummaging about the room she found no trace of what she was in search of. On the other hand she came across a satchel which contained a large amount of money. Some of it was coin, some was in the form of notes.

All the time she had been throwing glances at the owner of the house. She was afraid lest he awake, in which event she would turn round and find him watching her. And he would naturally think that she intended to appropriate the cash. Most probably, in his exasperation, he would see that here was no archangel and that he himself had fallen from the gate of heaven.

But Maria gradually grew more confident ; his coma was a very thorough one. He did not budge when she knocked down a little stool, against which she had stumbled in the sorry light.

The cat was moaning.

This would rouse the man, so that Maria ordered it to stop. And when it disobeyed she planted several kicks among the ribs of the poor creature.

It was I who now looked anxiously at the sick man, for how would he endure the shock of witnessing such unangelic conduct ? But he did not stir.

Maybe the cat imagined that Maria's kicks were

exhortations for it to stand up. At any rate, with a considerable effort, it arose and there is stood on most unsteady legs.

The door of the room opened. A young woman in a white blouse came towards us. " Is he . . . ? " she gasped out.

" No, no," Maria said. " He is alive."

" I am his daughter. Has he asked for me ? "

" Of course, of course he has. If you will kneel down," said Maria in a low voice, " I am certain he will bless you."

The young woman hastily crossed over to the bed and flung herself upon the floor. The skirt that she had on left visible the whole length of the peasant boots. Her father's hands were lying listlessly on the blue counterpane. She raised them to her lips and when she put them down again she fondled them. Her father did not know what she was doing.

Then his eyelids trembled. He was coming back into the world.

" I am Alzbeta, your Alzbeta," the young woman whispered.

Suddenly the man was wide awake and in a storm of fury. " Go," he cried. " My curses on you ! " And he strove to push her from the bed.

But the exertion was too much for him. As he fell back onto the pillow he was making incoherent noises in his throat, his face was livid.

And the cat began to howl.

This evidently pleased him, for with satisfaction written on his face he passed away.

The good Maria laid her hands on the young woman's head. She told her it was clear he had repented of his anger and that he had blessed her silently.

CHAPTER XV

WE spent that night, Maria and myself, at the vicarage. Our host was a very amiable old gentleman. He let his housekeeper, whose name was Božena, express herself as she desired regarding the dead man.

Božena was much upset, because she had been told that somebody was dying in the village, and she had not gathered who it was. But she had prayed for the salvation of that person's soul.

She was disgusted when she ascertained that it was Kuzma. " To think," she cried, " that I have been praying for him. Can I take it back, my prayer ? "

" He will have need of it," said the vicar.

" Such a miserable fellow," she explained to us. " In other days the people of this village used to go down to the plain, which now is Hungary, they used to go down at the harvest time and then they lived all the year on what they earned in those few weeks."

" It was a hard time for our people," said the vicar.

" And it was harder still," she said, " when nobody could go down there. The frontier ran between them and the plains. What did this Kuzma do ? He made them work for him. As they had nowhere else to go he paid them what he liked—and how much do you think he paid ? "

"But now," said the vicar, "we have had this land reform. The people are in a much better situation. There has been a tremendous improvement."

"That is true," she said, her voice quivering with bitterness. "Even the prisons have been improved. I have heard that the one in Bratislava has central heating in every cell, with a desk and a chair and an electric bell that goes on ringing, if you touch it, till the warder comes."

The vicar smiled. "Do you not approve," he asked, "of the new prison system?"

"I do not," she said emphatically, "and the reason is that Kuzma should have gone to prison, into one of those they used to have."

She turned and left the room.

I remained in the village all the next day, because the vicar said he would be much obliged if I would help in finding a suitable epitaph. Kuzma's daughter and her husband had requested him to put what he thought fit.

It was late in the afternoon when some of us—the vicar and the doctor and Maria and myself—went for a stroll. The doctor had made out Kuzma's death certificate, but the funeral had not yet taken place. This doctor gave one the idea that he could dress entirely in the dark, because he knew with absolute precision where in the wardrobe and the chest of drawers each item lay. There was no poetry, but also there was nothing vague in Dr. Kohut. One could see that by the way in which he walked. No doubt, as the old vicar said, he was a little justified in his impatience with the peasants, who were slow in their adoption of the new hygiene. Being the official doctor of three villages he came in contact with a goodly number of people.

" And confess now, Kohut," said the vicar, " that you find it hard to forgive them for being so healthy, in spite of their indifference to sanitation."

" They are an extraordinary people," said Kohut. " But I thought we were going to discuss the man's epitaph."

A bench, a few yards from the road, invited us to seat ourselves. It stood upon a rounded elevation, with a clump of trees behind it. In that evening light the pleasant country and the village had an air of peace. The columns of pale smoke were loitering on their way.

" Personally," said Dr. Kohut, who was at the end of our row, " I think it matters not at all what we inscribe upon his tombstone."

" Oh, please," said Maria—she was next to me and I was at the other end of the row—" please," she begged, " do not say that."

" But why not ? " asked the doctor.

" Because, oh because. . . ."

While she was searching for the reasons her neighbour on the right began to take a part in the discussion.

" What the Greeks were wont to do," he said, " was

to put the name of the dead person and append the words : ' Good man, happiness to you ! ' "

" We are not Greeks," said the doctor. " But that would be a nice inscription. There is such a monotony about our graveyards. In fact," said he to the vicar, " I have only one criticism of that Greek phrase of yours. It is not scientific. You are hoping that the man will have happiness, but his body is needed—every dead body sooner or later arises and takes part in the circulation of matter, so that your materials, for example, will enter over and over again into the composition of a variety of human bodies and therefore your bodily resurrection on doomsday is impossible. As you are here you will not be again."

" What do you say ? " exclaimed Maria. " Do you say that I will not go on for ever and ever ? What is to prevent me ? I ask you that."

" Chemistry," said the doctor. " It partly lifts the veil which hides the innermost nature of matter ; the old ideas vanish, they vanish even as the shadows of the night when it is dawn."

I had misjudged the man ; at any rate he had poetic moments.

" But all through my life," complained Maria, " I have been so certain that I will—if I conduct myself as I should do—that I will go among the blessed ones. And now you say that I may not have my own body, that it will be needed for some other people ! I am giddy when I even think of it."

" My friends," the vicar said, " we have not settled
yet what epitaph to have upon the tombstone."

" What you told us of the Greeks," said Dr. Kohut,
" that was very nice.   Those ancients were great
people."

" It was customary with the Romans," said the vicar,
" to adorn the monuments with pictures of the famous
exploits of the dead.   But if we want to do that for
this Kuzma, how shall we find any exploit worthy of
commemoration ?   So let the tombstone be a simple
one, with a few seemly words."

" For how long," said Maria, " will he roast ? "

" Do not be stupid.   Who can know a thing like
that ? " the doctor asked.

" But I can answer her," said the old clergyman.
" Do you perceive that smoke which rises from the
chimneys ?   It recalls the passage in the Scriptures
where one reads that ' the smoke of their torment goeth
up unto ages of ages.'   Now smoke is the formless relic
of that which has been decomposed by fire.   Ultimately
the fire burns itself out and there is no longer any tor-
ture for those who were condemned to punishment.
And so, whatever Kuzma may have done and even if
he has to roast unto ages of ages, I assure you that the
process will have an end."

" I am very glad to hear it," said Maria.

An old woman, with discoloured clothes, was drag-
ging towards the village a great mass of twigs and
branches she had gathered in the woods.   She halted

for a moment and from under her white eyebrows peered at us. Then she resumed her painful journey. None of us made any comment, so much were we occupied with our own problem.

CHAPTER XVI

WHEN Maria cut her fortunes off from mine, which operation happened in that village, she was kind enough to say that it was not because of anything in her or me. But ever since the death of Kuzma she was filled with dread of all the maladies which might attack her son.

I murmured that between her son and Kuzma there was no connection and that little Turčiansky, as she must have heard, possessed two centenarians; but if I could have come with the most glowing tables of statistics from the Ministry of Public Health it would have been in vain. She had resolved to go back hot-foot to the boy.

This conversation took place very early in the morning. Just as she had done that memorable day at Turčiansky, she abandoned ceremonial and came into my room.

I will not here repeat her touching and affectionate words, for in a little time she would be leaving me for ever. In this period of search-lights, we do still preserve, please God, some sanctities.

When I departed from that village it was with the vicar. He would see me safely on the way, he said.

As soon as we had started he began. He would not

have an opportunity of travelling to England. He was sorry. They must be a curious people.

" Perhaps," I said, " your expectations are too lofty and you might be disappointed if you went there."

" Do you think," he said, " that there are many of them like the members of the Eighty Club, which is a Liberal organisation ? The Eighty Club, or some of them, came here, you know, before the war, when all this land was under the Hungarians. Of course I do not mean that they came to the Slovak parts. They wanted to observe how Liberalism flourished in our State. They were superbly entertained and they were shown all kinds of things, such as the House of Parliament at Budapest, which architecturally is an imitation of the one in London. So they made enthusiastic speeches. They were very much in love with Hungary. And just about that time the most repressive laws were being passed in the Hungarian Parliament. The three remaining Slovak high-schools were shut up. Now if a party say of German Liberals or French should make a pilgrimage to England at the moment when she is suppressing all the schools where Welsh is taught ! "

" It would," I said, " be quite embarrassing."

" The members of the Eighty Club were not embarrassed," said the vicar. " On the contrary, they were delighted."

" But did no one tell them," I said, " that more than half the population of Hungary consisted of other nationalities, Slovaks, Roumanians and Serbs, and that while the Roumanians and the Serbs had Roumania and Serbia — independent countries — behind them to give them some sort of help, the Slovaks had nobody ? Were the Eighty Club so absolutely fooled ? "

" Let us hope so for their sake," said the vicar. He waved his stick at the landscape. " You will have a fine day," he remarked, " a day of driving clouds."

I told him I would need some compensation, now that I had to walk on without Maria.

" If only I were a younger man," said the vicar, " I would go all the way to Pišťany."

The time had come for the good vicar to go back, and I set forth alone, accompanied by the laughing wind, the sunlight and the race of clouds.

League followed league until I came to Pišťany. Beautiful is Pišťany with its parks of stately trees, the broad and rushing Waag, the music everywhere. The gipsy leader of the band that plays in the hotel asks only that he be allowed to play all night. From time to time he wanders round the room to play, as it were privately, into a lady's ear. He starts upon a tune he thinks appropriate, and his companions in the distant corner of the room chime in with him at once. The evening of my arrival a most prepossessing English lady novelist was being played to by this jovial gipsy ; what he played was " Tipperary." When she asked why she should be selected as the representative of the British army he replied that what he wanted to express was his desire to play for her alone and let the others all betake themselves to Tipperary.

Then we danced and one of the performers was a youthful German who had come some weeks before, so I was told, on crutches. These he subsequently had discarded for a stick and finally he took to dancing. One of the two brothers Winter who are the proprietors of Pištany—they are thinking all the time how they can make it the most perfect health resort in Europe— one of them was dancing too, a country dance more notable for zeal than languid grace ; and afterwards I heard that he has got a wooden leg.

He had no difficulty in persuading me to try the mud. The hot mud is applied to your prostrate body, under- neath it and, particularly, upon it, with such lavishness that you are as immovable as any fly in amber. And not only is a great thickness of mud plastered over you, but you are then wrapped very tightly in a sheet, so that you resemble a mummy.

Your meditations will be first devoted to the era of primeval slime, for does your present state not bring you back a good deal further than the mummies ? But if you are not a sufficiently devoted student of Mr. Wells—he knows, he knows !—did not the famous A. L. Smith, the Master of Balliol, say that the ' Outline of History ' is excellent until it reaches man ?—if you are not sufficient of a student, then you must, because you do not know the habits of those distant fauna, let your thoughts come to an epoch less remote. It is said that Pištany is mentioned in documents of the twelfth century, and good George Wernherus alludes to the hot springs and eke the mineral mud in a work of his that was published in 1551. Before the scientific method of obtaining the mud was introduced it must have been a most laborious process, seeing that it often is obtained from underneath the river Waag. We have the strange phenomenon of extremely hot mud—in its natural condition it is at 153 degrees Fahrenheit—which is to be had below the waters of an ordinary river. When the Waag, in the dry season of the year, diminishes in size, then a fair surface is exposed from which the mud is taken. But if the river does not shrink enough or if sufficient mud has not been stored, the rest must be obtained from underneath the river. Of course at the temperature of 153 degrees it is not applied to the patients ; it is cooled as much as necessary by having cold water thrown over it.

Perhaps by this time the moment has arrived for the attendant to liberate you. The mud will be removed from you by hand, assisted by the stream of a hot shower-bath which is behind every cubicle. You are escorted then to a huge swimming-bath of hot sulphur water, with mud upon the floor of it. You are requested not to swim, as the exertion would be harmful. But, clinging to the side or floating calmly on the surface, you have further opportunity for the continuation of historical researches. It may come into your memory that in the year 1642 Trajanus Bene-

shovianus wrote an ode entitled " Saluberrimae Pis-
tianensis Thermae." Regretfully you will admit that
you have not read this work ; but that omission, on
the other hand, allows you to speculate as to its con-
tents.

When you emerge from this steaming water you
undergo another shower-bath and proceed to be
swathed in towels and blankets. As you take your
ease for the allotted span—a clock in your cubicle is
set going and, to make doubly sure, a sand-glass is put
into operation—you are too exhausted, very plea-
santly exhausted, for the heights that were probably
attained in the Latin ode. You will lie there thinking
with gratitude about the mud which has taken the
trouble to come up from a distance of 1,500 feet. You
will think, perhaps, of Beethoven or some of the other
great men who have in the past brought their rheumatic
limbs and their neuralgias and neuritis to the home of
mud. Even as at Lourdes, there is here a museum of
discarded crutches. Whether the invalid is to betake
himself to Lourdes or to Pištany must be left to his
individual discretion.

If you are not in one of the two main hotels that
stand upon the island in the river and adjoin the baths,
it is delightful to be taken back to where you live in a
kind of Sedan chair on wheels. It is pulled by a sturdy
native, male or female, who is arrayed in the picturesque
national costume. These Sedan chairs have existed
certainly from the Napoleonic era ; they are, for some

reason, called " Infanterists," and, being provided with a curtain behind the window, they allow one to go from this extreme of retirement almost into the extreme of publicity which is preferred by those who return on foot in their pyjamas. And whether you are among the former or the latter nobody takes any special notice of you.

To be at Pištany after having lived among the simple Slovak people was an odd experience. Certainly you are not so divorced from your environment as on a modern liner, where lest you forget that you are on the sea, you have deliberately to take a look at it. Amid the cosmopolitan amenities of Pištany with the fascinating little shops, the streets of asphalt and the flower beds, the shaded promenades where you can hear a dozen languages, the tennis players and the fishermen you will not easily forget that you are in Slovakia. I found more of the lovely native costumes than in other places, and although they are encouraged to display themselves in this attire, which is conducive to a slight self-consciousness, yet that is better than to see no costumes. And from time to time one comes upon inscriptions in pure Slovak, such as that one on a sign-post, with a finger pointing out the way : " Za Golfu."

I was strolling idly by the river-side the second afternoon a trifle grieved because I had no rheumatism.

" Yes, sir ? " It was said in German, the international language of south-eastern Europe and the Balkans.

I looked round. Who was the owner of this pleasant voice ? It was a young man sitting on a bench that otherwise was empty. He got up and bowed in the politest way, he would have taken off his hat if he had worn one. His figure, which was passing stout, was garbed in sombre, inconspicuous clothes.

" Have you lost anything ? " he asked. " Of course I know that you have not lost at roulette, because you have not been there. I am an official of that room, in fact the croupier. But have you lost something else ? You look unhappy."

" It is kind of you," I said. " May I sit down a little ? " Then I told him that I rather felt that I was there on false pretences, like a Peri who should not have entered Paradise.

" You have no rheumatism ? ".

" Once," I told him, " in the Orkneys I made the acquaintance of a clergyman who served three islands. He was a poor sailor and, to keep himself from being sick, he used to take a certain remedy if there was any sea at all. One day when he had swallowed it he walked down to the harbour and discovered that the waves were too high for the boat to leave. The clergyman went home, where he was sick."

My croupier's shoe was moving sideways, very thoughtfully. And then he said that he had never heard of anyone partaking of the Pištany cure and getting rheumatism if beforehand he was free from it. One could not have a bath, he said, without a doctor's written order and a man who had no rheumatism would be only given a slight treatment. " But," he said more cheerfully, " one of the doctors told me that in England, which is damp and foggy, half the population have some rheumatism in their systems."

" What do you recommend me to do ? " I asked.

" Of course," he answered, " I am a croupier and not a doctor. Did the doctor tell you that you have no rheumatism and that he would let you have a bath as an experience ? "

" That is so," I said.

Again his meditative foot moved to and fro. " You might return to him," he said, " and tell him you believe you are rheumatic."

" But if he assures me I am not ? "

" Well," said the croupier, " you cannot argue with him. For one thing, I suppose, it is not etiquette. And if he will not let you be rheumatic, then you must be honest. Tell him that his diagnosis is, as a matter of fact, wonderful and that you would like to have a few experimental baths. For how long do you want to stay ? "

" Four or five days," I said. " That is all I can spare."

" Then you have no time," said the croupier, " for any rheumatism. But you can have a little gamble if you come to-night at ten o'clock to that hotel." He pointed through the trees.

" Is it very exciting ? "

He reassured me and said that, on the contrary, it was rather tame, which was, I felt, the natural attitude for croupiers. The fortunes won and lost do not concern him. And the whole thing must become exceedingly monotonous.

It was even more so for this croupier than I had imagined, because when I sat down that night among the seven or eight players I noticed that one of them, sitting opposite the croupier, pressed a button which electrically sent the little white ball on its business. " Rien ne va plus " and the other phrases were spoken by the croupier. Thus, by Czechoslovak law, he took a modest part in the proceedings and the stakes were modest too. Most of the players seemed to lose, especially the one who set the ball in motion. But they were quite happy.

When the room was closed the croupier and I went back to where we first had met. I saw that he had something on his mind and that his wish to breathe some fresh air was a pretext.

The long promenade beside the river lay in moonlight. You could see so clearly the white foam and the grey waters as they hurried past.

" You see," he said, " how dull it is."

I had to make a protest.

Then he said he was alluding to his life. " Those

men who go down the river—we have not seen any of them, as it happens—on their huge rafts going down for days and days. Their life is different. It is a splendid life ! "

" But," I said, " with drawbacks."

" One day in low water gliding past the meadows, on the next day navigating through the rocks and rushing, rushing onward. What a dreary life is mine ! "

I took his arm and guided him into a sheltered alcove, probably intended for an invalid. There it was warm enough to sit.

The croupier's face was full of gloom. He said that he had seen me looking at him in the house.

" I thought," I said, " that you are capable of higher things. And if you are dissatisfied that is all to the good. You understand me ? "

" No," said he.

Then I was at a loss how to continue, for I had no notion of what higher things the man was capable. He had appeared to me a somewhat ordinary man.

" If there had not been a great storm," he said regretfully, " when I was on my father's farm I would have been a farmer too."

" The place was devastated, I suppose ? " said I.

" Yes, and my father, like the rest of them, owed so much money to the bank that he could get no more. An uncle who was living in a town took care of me and I was sent to school. That was the first step towards becoming what you see me now. Oh, the grand storm ! " he said.

To my surprise he seemed to revel in that memory. I did not have to ask him to say more about it.

" Sixty hours on end it raged," said he, " the shrieking gale, the rattle of the windows and the cruel sleet. My father and the other men had not a moment's rest, they struggled out to feed the ewes and lambs—some of them were in barns and some were in the orchard, some were sheltering among the carts. Everyone was hard at work except the sheep-dogs, who were lying by the stove on mats we used to make of reeds out of the swamp. A dog or two lay underneath his master's chair and now and then he came up to the stove and stretched himself and growled with pleasure and went back. For them it was a holiday. They would be of no use at such a time and it was dangerous, besides, to let them out. You see, the carcases of the dead ewes and lambs are often left for days unburied—the chief difficulty was to save the lambs, although the shepherds with their flickering lanterns battled with the storm and carried many of them in, their legs all stiff, their yellow bodies shivering and, at the shepherd's heel, the bleating mother—but too many of them perished, the poor lambs dropped in the slush, so that my father used to say that if they were not on their feet within two minutes they would have their death of cold. We did our best to find protection for the ewes who would be dropping lambs. But we were always hearing of some others who were lost. The shepherds were so busy that they could not bury them at once and so the foxes and the ravens and the wolves would have their orgies. That is when a sheep-dog, wandering about the country, may be tempted to become a mutton-eater. He must be destroyed. The hand of everybody is against him, for the chances are that this illicit meat will turn into his ruling passion and that he will raid the living flocks. Well, in our farm we had a most beloved dog and he did that and he was to be shot."

The croupier paused and, for the second time, I was astonished. He had spoken of the dog with deep affection ; now he was exultant.

" Did you know," he said, " the dogs will visit one another on a day when they have nothing else to do ? From time to time one meets a dog upon a mountain trail and he is going to a farm a long way off. Our dog who was to die had a great friend who lived in the next valley. They were the two biggest dogs in all the countryside. The name of our dog, owing to the colour of his coat, was Grey ; we did not know the farmer who possessed the other dog and so we never learned the creature's name."

" But I suppose," I said, " that in the storm you spoke about there was no visiting ? "

" I am just going to tell you," said the croupier. " I had overheard them and I knew the plan that was decided on—my father would shoot Grey himself.

He loved him, I believe, almost as much as I did. In the middle of that fearful storm, while he was losing nearly every lamb and while the house was being torn apart and it was ruin and disaster everywhere, he seized his gun and said that he would not come back before he had shot Grey. I was a youngster at the time, a rebel. I told no one, but I swore that I would rescue Grey and even if he had become a mutton-eater."

It was wonderful to see the croupier's face beside me in the moonlight, for the sorrows of it had evaporated.

" When my father left the house not only with the gun but with a spade," he said, " I followed him and no one saw me. It was between two and three o'clock of the afternoon, but in that howling tempest it was nearly dark. My father went up the main track—he knew that Grey would come on that road, going home. At first I could not think—the snow was like sharp arrows and they flew at me from every quarter. I tried walking backwards for a step or two. How could I get to Grey, so as to warn him ? I believed that he was at the other farm, visiting his friend."

" How did you know," I said, " that he was not eating mutton somewhere in the fields ? "

" My Grey would not do such a thing," he said indignantly. " It had occurred, but only once."

" If that was so," I said, " how could your father shoot him ? He must have believed quite differently."

" And even if my Grey had been a criminal a

thousand times," he said, " I would have fought for him. I was in agony—he might be coming back and what could I do then ? . . . I was quite near my father—he concealed himself amid a group of rocks. The people say that men were sacrificed in there, because of a religion. That was long ago—and now he wanted to kill Grey and that, I felt, was just as horrible. I went behind the rocks, up to the track again and on and on, in spite of all the tempest. Luckily the track was not completely covered, owing to the way the wind was blowing. . . . Now I did not have to rush along, because if Grey arrived I could take hold of him. Then I would lead him to the other farm and ask them if they would be kind enough to keep him. How I would approach the farmer and exactly how I would begin the conversation gave my thoughts a lot of work, so that I did not notice what good progress I was making. How would I reply if someone at the farm should ask me for my reason ? Could I say that Grey was ill and needed some companionship ? And if they kept him, what about this mutton-eating ? It would not be honourable if I was silent. I could say that he had suffered from it once and that they must be good to him and so he would be altogether cured. . . . As I plodded on I was rehearsing everything that I would say and also how the people there would answer."

" When you reached the farm," I said, " no doubt your preparations were of little value."

" No one knew me," said the croupier, " except Grey.

He put his paws upon my shoulders and he licked me joyfully. But how could anyone, I thought, look in those faithful eyes and still assert he was a mutton-eater ? I explained from where I was and asked them, as I had arranged to do, that they should let Grey live among them, for a time at any rate. They were astonished. Then I suddenly determined that their dog must come with me—I waited till I was alone with the two dogs. I told Grey he must lie down and be very quiet—then I put a string into the collar of the other one and he came with me."

" He came with you just like that ? " I said.

" Fortunately," said the croupier, " he was stupid. And he was a hero. Very soon we got away from all the buildings of that farm and now I gloried in the sleet and snow—they were the most enchanting kisses and my heart was so full that I could not sing. We climbed up to the higher ground—the storm became more furious than ever—twice it knocked me down, the second time I was in a deep snow-drift, but the dog pulled at the string and got me out. He started pulling me along the track, as if he knew where we were going to."

" Then he was not so stupid, after all ? " I said.

The croupier smiled a little wanly. " In comparison with Grey," said he, " the dog was stupid. But he was a splendid animal and I will not forget him while I live. As I was telling you, we pushed across the elevated ground—one could not see more than an arm's length ;

but at last I knew that we were near the rocks in which my father was. He would be there still, I felt quite certain. But I was not certain that he would shoot properly—he would be so excited and his fingers would be cold. I fastened up the dog onto a stone and then I ran to where my father was. I told him I had gone for Grey and brought him back. My father said that he was proud of me. What would I have as a reward ? He knew how fond I was of Grey and it was dutiful of me, he said, to help, especially on such a day. I asked him if he would allow me, after Grey was shot, to bury him myself, and he consented. . . . In his pocket he had got some string, which I took back with me, to make a longer line ; and then I thought it would be well to go not on the track but half-way up the bank beyond it, where my father through the snow-flakes would not see that I had brought a stranger dog. And everything occurred just as I planned it. When the dog was dead my father shouted at me that he had a spade there in the rocks, that I could fetch it and he would not interfere with me."

The croupier stopped, as if the loose ends of the tale were not worth gathering up. Presumably his father's fortunes crashed with such completeness that the boy went off without delay to his kind uncle in the town ; presumably the new proprietor of Grey accepted him in lieu of his own dog and did not undertake a useless prosecution ; and presumably the story ended there, the most romantic story in the croupier's life. He had been so much absorbed in telling me about it that his previous discontent had vanished.

I was in the act of rising when he laid a hand upon my arm.

" That is not all," he said, " oh, no, that is not all." His laugh was like the moonlight in the little eddies of the river.   " Often I can see them racing, the two dogs, and as they run they gambol with each other.   I can see them on a night like this and when it is the clearest daylight I can see them too.   Now my beloved Grey will dart ahead and then the other one.   They know what there is waiting for them in the rocks.   And when they are in sight of them the gambolling is finished. Now they race—their long legs hardly touch the ground —their eyes are blood-shot and the foam hangs from their jaws—it is the finest race that ever has been— on and on—Grey takes the lead and then the other flings himself in front—and then I hear them gasping in triumph : ' I—I win ! ' exclaims the one. ' No, I ! ' exclaims the other. And the blades of grass are shouting at them and the pebbles on the ground . . ."

CHAPTER XVII

THOSE who examine countries from a railway carriage or a motor-car will frequently look down their nose at the pedestrian. His progress, they allege, is at so poor a speed that by the time he has attained his destination all the circumstances at the other end of his itinerary may have altered. A more serious objection is that such a man is not a serious traveller, since he does not procure his facts from the official sources, but attempts to do so from whatever people he may chance to meet, with the result that he will gather a great deal which cannot be described as fact.

Ah, yes, to trust to your own feet exposes you to many dangers. But of all pedestrians one should commiserate, I think, especially with those who never, never will be non-pedestrians. While they are walking they pay less attention to the landscape and the human figures than to their own satisfaction at the leagues which they have covered. What are they but slaves? The true pedestrian is surely he who is devoid of prejudice against the other travellers and who will, if so it seemeth good to him, employ their means of locomotion. Dullness of the scenery should not be the unique, or even the main, cause of the pedestrian's abandonment, for the time being, of the use of his feet ; a more weighty reason should be the dullness of mood. Which of us has not traversed a grand Alpine gorge and been indifferent to the sublimity ? That is when one ought to avail oneself of carriages and trains and aeroplanes. From Pištany to Bratislava I went by train.

For administrative purposes it is unfortunate that Slovakia's capital, Bratislava, lies in the south-west corner of the country, a very few miles from the Austrian and Hungarian frontiers. But the presence of the Danube gives to Bratislava the predominant advantage over all the other Slovak towns ; and when we stand there on the station platform, rather high above the main part of the city, we can see, to right and left of us, the rising, undulating ground with many stately buildings on it—obviously schools and other institutions—and whole colonies of charming villas. Everyone says to himself that if he had arrived at Bratislava, say in 1919 or in 1920, he would have perceived immediately that this expansion must occur and that the value of the land would multiply. An admirable grape was on those hills, so that the farmers in the old days were contented with their lot ; but such of them as did not in the first years of the new State sell their land were able afterwards to reap a very golden harvest.

If an Englishman will look about him at the station he will be most gratified, for Bratislava is delicious

" They do," said Mr. Wolny. " Let me see—yes,
1477 Slovak farmers have been settled in 25 new
villages and in 16 that existed before. Some of these
colonies are in Slovak districts where the villages were
very far apart. Others are in the Hungarian regions.
I think it is right that the Slovak peasants with their
greater need—the old Government was rather a step-
mother towards them—it was they more than the
Hungarians who always emigrated—I think it is right
if they are favoured a little and if they are brought
down from the mountains. I do not quite understand
how a small number of Slovak farmers will denationalize
300,000 Hungarians. I should have thought it will be
the other way about. But some of the Hungarian
deputies and lawyers, here in Czechoslovakia, are most
apprehensive."

" I suppose," I said, " that the people themselves
get on fairly well with each other ? "

Mr. Wolny smiled. " I am afraid," said he, " that
they get on a good deal too well for many of my countrymen in Hungary. Their services as Hungarian pro-
pagandists are lost for ever. They like the Slovak
farmers and the Slovak authorities. Over in Hungary
it is a rural custom for the peasant, decked out in gaily-
coloured ribbons, to march behind his master to the
place where the deputy is elected and of course the
peasant echoes his master's voice. In this Republic
the ballot is secret, with the result that there are some
fourteen Hungarian deputies. They can use their own

language, if they like, in the Parliament at Prague ;
but as it is not generally known up there they have a
habit of saying a sentence or two in Hungarian and
then continuing in German. As I told you, this country
has about fourteen Hungarian deputies, but the 200,000
Slovaks in Hungary have not a single representative
in the Budapest Parliament. These contrasts are so
flagrant that it is not surprising if the Hungarian over
here is very cheerful."

" But," I asked, " how can open elections be justified
at this time of day ? "

" The excuse which is always made," said Mr.
Wolny, " is that the people have not sufficient education—and whose fault is that ? They would fall an
easy prey, so the Hungarian Government asserts, to
the blandishments of the Russian Bolsheviks and the
Viennese Socialists. Personally," he said, " I of course
prefer the latter and maybe even the former to that
feudal Government, the most reactionary in Europe,
which now holds the fort in Budapest against the
majority of the nation. I hope," he said, " I have not
wearied you. One gets carried away. It was only last
week that we had an amusing illustration of how comfortable the Hungarian farmers feel in this country.
There was a cattle-show at the Slovak colony of
Maczhaza, near Komorno, and the Hungarians from
the neighbouring villages were invited, some of them
were put on the juries. It was optional to take one's
prize in money, as was done by most of the Slovaks,

or to have a diploma, which the Hungarians asked for and despite the fact that they were printed in the Slovak language. The Hungarians were going to hang them up as decorations in their homes."

It was indeed most fortunate that I had met this gentleman.

He shrugged his shoulders and said very modestly that if we had not come across each other I would have got all these facts from someone else.

" But that I should have met you," I said, " even before going to an hotel."

" And now you will not go to one," said Mr. Wolny. " I have got a room for you, because my son is absent."

While I was endeavouring to decline his hospitality, as I was anxious not to inconvenience him, he talked of other matters.

" It is my opinion," he said, "—I do not know if it is yours—that if one wishes for a thing extremely one obtains it."

" There must be," I said, " some good hotels in Bratislava. Why should I not . . ."

" It is quite mysterious," said Mr. Wolny, " how one does obtain it. I believe that people signal to each other, though they do not know it. One is making signals and another person in the crowd replies and so they come together. Shall we go now ? "

When we left the café and were walking through a little park I felt that if I made another effort to refuse his invitation I would hurt him.

Suddenly he darted from me. He had seen, outside the park, a picturesque old personage with a slouch hat and a fine mane of hair. He caught him up, conferred with him and then the picturesque one went his way.

" I have arranged it for you," Mr. Wolny said as he came back. " To-morrow after three o'clock he hopes to see you. It is Professor Kolisek, one of the features of this town. He is the head of the Catholic Theological College, but as he is appointed by the Government the Vatican withholds its sanction. So the college is not operating and the doctor travels round the country in pursuit of folk-songs."

We were walking on the esplanade beside the Danube, which at Bratislava is a swift and, at the same time, a majestic river. The inhabitants have made the best of both worlds, for they have laid out a series of delightful walks along the bank, while further down they have created a considerable harbour, where the imports and the exports leap from year to year. The University, the Government office and various other fine buildings overlook the river. As we arrived at the Government office—a very large affair—Mr. Wolny stopped. He told me that the porters and the messengers, the clerks and secretaries and the Minister for Slovakia had a rather disturbed morning one day in the early years of the Republic.

" They looked out of their windows towards the bridge," he said, " which, as you see, is quite close. It is the only bridge in this part of the river, it is used for railway and all other traffic. But on that morning a number of Hungarians were half way across the bridge and from there they tried to persuade Bratislava to shake off the Czechoslovak yoke. They were assisted by an aeroplane which threw leaflets ; and the Hungarians in the town did not know what would happen. The authorities had very few soldiers at their disposal, yet they managed to induce the Hungarians to go back to their side of the river and about twenty of the chief Hungarians in the town were taken up country and interned in a villa."

" So it all passed off," I said, " without any damage being done ? "

" Some of those who were interned," said Mr. Wolny, " were not satisfied that they had to pay for their food, although they admitted that the charge was moderate. And then there was heart-burning in the town—some Hungarians, who considered that they were among the most influential, were left at liberty. This they regarded as an insult."

I asked if there had been any other demonstrations on the bridge and Mr. Wolny told me that the frontier had been fixed a mile or two beyond the other bank.

" But, nevertheless," he said, " in spite of what Foch brought about in this case, so that there should for the future be no disturbances, we still have incidents from time to time. All men are not created in the image of

Solomon. There is a certain official, a Slovak, who in the old days was in the government service far down in Hungary. He assumed a most Hungarian name. Outside his office he put up a notice to the effect that he was to be addressed exclusively in Hungarian. This he did of his own initiative, out of sheer patriotism. He married a Hungarian lady. When the war was at an end he returned to Slovakia . . ."

" And to his Slovak name ? " I asked.

" No, he did not do that," said Mr. Wolny. " He was given a high post and in the town which he adminstered he forbade that the Hungarian language should be used even in private conversation. His wife was too old to learn Slovak, and that day at dinner she spoke not a word ; the children followed her example. When the furious man went out into the street some of the citizens, who only knew a phrase or so of Slovak, barked at him as if they had been dogs."

Meanwhile we had struck northward from the river. We were walking down the street where Mr. Wolny lived. When he had taken me up to his flat he said that he would have to leave me for an hour or two, as he had a professional appointment.

" That reminds me," he said. " We were talking of the Land Office and I should like to tell you of another little thing they did. There was a Slovak called Gessay who came from America and founded an American-Slovak League. They bought an estate from Count

Albert Apponyi and founded two colonies, Gessayovo and Thomašovo. The Land Office made them offer a fair proportion of the land to the local Hungarians. . . . Now I must be going. How will you amuse yourself till I return ? I have a goodish library and the servant, when you wish, will bring you tea—but perhaps you don't like China tea ? "

" I am sorry I am not a connoisseur," I said.

" A friend of mine obtains it through the Soviet Legation. It comes overland from China, as it should do, on the backs of camels."

" I am still more sorry," I said, " that I am not a connoisseur."

" In that room opposite," said Mr. Wolny, " is a shower-bath."

But I resolved that I would tear myself away from these delights when Mr. Wolny counselled me to go at once if I desired to see the Protestant Hungarian bishop. Mr. Wolny was himself a Protestant and now, he said, I would find Bishop Ballog at his home. Possibly the reader recollects how much I had been looking forward to this interview.

" He is a benevolent old man," said Wolny as we started off again.

Beside the church, whose exterior at all events is uncompromising, a grey covered passage has been built. Here my companion left me. I went on and, after walking through the passage, found myself confronted by a little courtyard and a house of sordid aspect, very like a tenement. A notice at the doorway said that Bishop Ballog lived upstairs. As I was reading this a man who seemed to be a concierge or factotum watched me from a room where he was sitting with his wife and children. He was in his shirt-sleeves of dark flannel and he very courteously refrained from putting on his coat, so that I should not have to wait. We mounted to the second floor, with children garnishing the staircase. He informed me that they did not all belong to him, but far too many of his countrymen, he said, preferred to have one child.

" The Slovak villages," said he, " up in the mountains, and not even in the mountains, you should see them. There the fields are so divided into narrow strips, one strip for every son, that it appears impossible to work them. I believe that with regard to children . . ."

He had pulled a bell and at this moment it was answered by a youth who ushered me into a large and austere room. Two men were sitting at a table face to face, a younger man was hovering in the background. It was obvious who was Bishop Ballog, though he did not seem to be in clerical attire. His body gave one the impression of diffuseness, while his look was amiable and pathetic.

After we had told each other who we were he introduced me to his secretary, a most dapper person with his black hair parted in the middle. As for the young man, he was a student of theology, about to enter a

great institute in Strasbourg. He was very unflam-
boyant.

Bishop Ballog spoke on various topics :

" Well," said the Bishop of the Calvinist Hungarian
    Church,
(A dear old man who had been in America)
" Well," he said, " it sure might be worse for us,
That is for Magyars in this new Republic.
But there is one thing that we want,
We want a Magyar University."

He rolled his eyes. " It is the truth," he said,
" That you could find some faults in other days :
We did not give the Slovaks Slovak lessons.
No, not even when they were announced
In the curriculum."
" Poor folk," said I, " they wanted their own
    tongue."
" We want," he said, " our University."

" Yes, I have heard," he said, " I have been told
That now and then a Slovak was expelled
Because of entertaining Slovak thoughts
And others on account of talking Slovak."
" But now you talk just what you like," I said.
" We talk about our University."

I asked the dear old man, was he aware
That Hungary with her eight million folk
Has got four Universities to-day,
Whereas 700,000 Magyars dwell
Here in Slovakia. . . . " But they don't possess,"
He pointed out, " a University."

CHAPTER XVIII

IN the crowded state of Professor Kolisek's apartment it was impossible for him to change the position of his zither-table. So while he was playing, which he did most vigorously, I looked at his broad back, his grey locks falling over it and, more especially, his arms that were as the two piston-rods of an express locomotive. He wanted me to hear some of the Slovak folk-songs he has gathered. As he struck the clanging wires he was pouring out the words and, for his age, I thought he was an admirable singer. Would that my appreciation had been half as perfect for the national liqueur which he had given me. The name of it was borovička. He had told me, as he smilingly produced a bottle that this white liqueur is made out of the juniper. I took a sip and found it stronger than I bargained for.

The Professor was engaged upon a song—a girl says she must once again look at the garden-hedge behind which is the home of her beloved ; she must call him once again.

Where could I throw the borovička ? The old man might turn round at any moment. Therefore I must stay in the armchair in which he had installed me ; and besides, imprisoned as I was by a large table and with an Italian reredos a foot or so away from it and with a picture of my host in Slovak costume—a new acquisition, he had told me—leaning up against the table, I could not rise very noiselessly. The borovička oubliette would have to be some flower-pot, because the soil —in expiation of that guilty soil from which the juniper had sprung—would drink it. But there was no flower-pot, there was absolutely nothing that I could use.

In the cool of dawn, so the Professor sang, the maiden gave her hand to the beloved ; but before they could take leave of one another she had fallen in his arms and she was dead.

If I had to take this borovička I would surely die. That Japanese lieutenant in the sunken submarine who wrote from hour to hour what he was feeling, until he, like all his comrades, had succumbed—that officer should be my model. I would write——

Then her mother asked the girl whether God would be kind to her. She answered that in Zvolen graveyard He was giving her a house.

I took another sip. Who was the demon who invented this concoction ? To what graveyard would they carry me ? What would the Professor say when he turned round and ascertained that I was dead ? Considering that I had only just made his acquaintance he might well resent the liberty which I had taken. He would be distressed, but if he likewise harboured some resentment he would be entirely justified. One should not pass away in someone's room when he is doing what he can to please you. And particularly you should not let it be known that the disaster happened through your host's liqueur. But he would find that out when I was dead. In fact it would be preferable if I were to stay alive.

There, said the maiden, I will go to have my sleep and there the music will encompass me, the beautiful young cavaliers will dance around me.

If, I thought, if I had been going to die this was a place as suitable as any, with the holy pictures hanging on the walls and little ones propped up in various places. Also, here and there, lay bits of woodwork which had once been in a church and sacred vessels of good beaten silver hung upon a screen or shared a shelf with some of the domestic vessels.

And the little stars in Heaven, so the maid—that is Professor Kolisek—was singing, yes the little stars will be my comrades. The All-Highest, he will be my darling.

That was where the song concluded. I had written not a single word of my sensations on the grisly road. But as there had been this reprieve and I was, after all, not going on the journey, it appeared to be more modest that I should refrain from putting down what had occurred, when I had only travelled such a little distance.

" But you do not like it ? " the Professor asked.

" Oh yes, yes. It has made me dream," I said.

" And thank you very much. Will you give me another one ? "

" Well, we have thirty thousand. Help yourself to
borovička."

As he played and sang some others a black doubt
swept over me. This walk of mine had been so brief
and I had covered such a small part of the country.
People will arise and say that it was more than bold
of me to write about Slovakia when I had not so much
as visited a certain town. If I should answer that the
life led by the natives of the place will be no different
from that of other places in Slovakia I run the risk
of being told that this is mere surmise. And if I
humbly say that I have no pretention to describe
Slovakia, but only regions of it, then I shall be asked
would Mr. So-and-So and Mr. So-and-So, supposing
that they were to take my route, would they see just
what I had seen ? That, I would have to answer, is
unlikely.

The Professor ceased. He started off at once upon
another song.

The story of a journey might, indeed, be like a peal
of bells, a peal just a little way off and heard over the
snows.

" Are you conscious," said the Professor, turning
round abruptly, " of the new Slovak song ? It is the
greatest of them all." He smote the air with his right
wand. He threw his head back in defiance and this
made him look extremely leonine. " It is the song of

youth," he said, " that rises everywhere. I listen to it—I am passionately happy and I brush away the tears. O youth, now in your freedom you will shoulder any task and even if it be too great. The chorus of the young men can be heard—they are advancing—the young men who have been dedicated to the service of the Slovak land. The time is drawing near. Please help yourself to borovička."

" Let me pour you out a glass," I said. He was so in the sway of his emotions that when I filled up my own glass he accepted it—he raised it to his lips. I took an empty one—this borovička has a splendid quality, its whiteness—and our glasses touched.

" So let us drink to young Slovakia ! " he cried.

But if I had done so and with nothing in my glass who knows what cloud-burst of calamities would have resulted ? What the penalty exactly is for drinking to a person with an empty glass I was not sure. But I felt certain that it would be drastic, for there are some things that simply are not done and one of them is running counter to tradition. Probably the gods who mete out punishment would be so furious at a solecism such as mine that they would not distinguish closely between my guilt and the guilt of young Slovakia. How terrible if these young men, just at the time of their magnificent endeavour, should have this exasperation visited upon them. What I had to do and instantly was to perform the ritual prescribed. Alas, I did not know what steps to take. It might not help

the Slovaks in the least if I were to pick up the glass
and let it drop, like a golf ball, behind my back. If I
were to fling it across my left shoulder then perhaps
I should be satisfying the gods who preside over the
folk-lore of the Estonians, while those who are in
charge of the Slovak department would be, if anything,
more hostile than ever. A swift decision had to be made.

" Boleráz, Boleráz, village where the hills are green."
The Professor's face was radiant as he broke into this
celebrated song. " Stay with me, beloved ; you must
not leave to-day . . . Now you go on," he said.
" However, if you do not know the words then I will.
This is it : Yes, I will stay to-night, my sweetest dove.
But you must waken me at earliest dawn."

" I am sorry," I said. " Thank you for everything,
but I must go." I had resolved to hurry to a café
and drink three times to the young Slovaks. This, I
might hope, would turn the anger of the gods.

" You have not heard the end of the song," said the
Professor.

" No, it sounds," I said, " as if it would be tragic.
What you were saying of the young Slovaks so elated
me that really I——"

" In that case," he agreed, " I must let you go. Farewell."

Some hours later I was by the side of Mr. Wolny
at the opera. He told me something that I made a
note of on my programme. There is a place called
Kesztölcz with a population of 2,179, a hundred of whom

are Hungarians. Kesztölcz contains 425 children and of these about twenty are Hungarians. In the school the Slovaks have the first floor, the Hungarians the second. The history books and reading books are printed in Slovak on one side, with the other in Hungarian.

" The other day at dinner," Mr. Wolny smiled, " a beautiful compatriot of mine assured me that in Slovak schools they teach the children that it is quite mediaeval to have kings, because Hungary is a Kingdom, though the throne is vacant. She said they teach that of course England is a republic and that the last Hungarian King, who died a year or so ago, was St. Stephen."

" And she really believed in the existence of that kind of school ? " I asked.

" You will regard it as impossible," said Mr. Wolny, " that the same country can have such a fantastic school as that and the school at Kesztölcz. But I should think the lady has never been inside a village school and she may quite well have believed the tale she told me."

I said it seemed a pity.

But Mr. Wolny did not acquiesce. He said that if you have no shadow you can have no sun ; and because it has a side that we regret are we to banish all imagination ? " For example," he said, " there would be less gaiety in Budapest if the Sz. M.E., the Union of Slovak Emigrants, did not exist."

He saw that I was puzzled.

"No," he said, "they are not a circus or a cabaret, but an evening with them, I should think, must be very comic. Not one of the chiefs talks a word of Slovak, though some of them may be of Slovak origin. They left Slovakia for various reasons and their object is to demonstrate to the world that Slovaks have been expelled from their own province and are not allowed to return. I must really go to one of their meetings," said Mr. Wolny, "the next time I am in Budapest. But when they speak of their old home more in anger than in sorrow and speak exclusively in Hungarian I hope I shall be able to suppress my laughter."

I asked him whether he had no ambition to be another Cervantes and laugh away the Sz. M.E. as the great man laughed away the dreary books of chivalry.

He said he would deplore it if, for instance, the Czechoslovak Communists were to be routed in that or any other way. They will leave the world a less diverting place. "Consider them in Bohemia and Moravia," he said, "where they tell the police beforehand of their meetings. They are the most orderly of all the parties. I am afraid that in the rural, eastern parts of the Republic they will not have the success which they enjoyed at the last General Election. Do you know what they did? They went into the villages and appealed not to the voter's heads but to their feet; they insisted on taking measurements and they promised everyone a pair of boots. If they go back to those villages in order to explain their programme the promises about the boots will have to be explained away. Yes, they have made it difficult for themselves. But it would not be the first serious obstacle they have survived. They did something or other which Moscow disapproved of, and in their own newspapers they had to print what Moscow thought of them."

When the opera was finished and we streamed out to the cool and gracious night we turned our steps towards the hills that look down in a brooding semi-circle on the city. All those lighted windows far away were like a multitude of bees and they were scattered on the foothills and the middle slopes. Beyond them one perceived, under a pale sky, those loftier, remoter woods and meadows. Up among them it would be delightful to look down and contemplate. The noises of the opera, our own included, would be all forgotten in the sacred silence of the hills. As we went through the shrouded market-place and past Bishop Ballog's church—now in the night made almost lovable—we did not speak. And the few solitary wayfarers seemed to be more intent on bed than on enjoying the great marvels of that night.

But Mr. Wolny of a sudden made an exclamation and as he turned down a narrow street I followed him. Here one beheld more people than were in the main street and the squares. They were not solitary either, but in couples and small groups, and they appeared to have no sorrows. Those who knew each other, going up and down the street, saluted in a very friendly fashion ;

but of greater interest to the observer was the attitude of them who happened to be unacquainted. As they passed each other they would glow with sympathy.

Some persons came out of a house which had a pole projecting from the door. But we went in and I observed that this was not the house-door but the one from which, on ordinary days, the cart emerged. And all the passage was filled up with benches and with tables, occupied by many people. Everyone was drinking wine.

" They may sell it for a fortnight, their own wine," said Mr. Wolny. " For a fortnight they can sell without the middleman, the inn-keeper. They put it in the papers when they exercise their rights, these owners of the vineyards."

What we drank was not one of those lyric wines the name of which makes music in the heart of man ; still less was it a great, historic wine that one approaches with solemnity. In fact, although no doubt it had a name, I did not hear it. All I knew was that the glass contained a golden-coloured, jolly liquid. It was very young and, surely, it was very innocent.

Moreover in the next house Mr. Wolny took me to, which was conveniently opposite the first one, we had placed before us a most charming little wine that blended, I discovered, with its predecessor. But, so far as Mr. Wolny was concerned, the two wines were inimical to one another.

He was all for going home. But the mood that I was

in demanded that I should bestride the world's roof or, at any rate, those hills.

So in the narrow street he gave me various instructions as to how I should proceed. Yet he was not as lucid as he might have been ; perhaps I did not listen very patiently.

When he had gone it seemed to me that I would not lose much if I were to forget his muddled phrases of advice. I therefore tried the vintage in two other houses of that street. I found them both quite satisfactory. And then I started for the main street and the hills. My soul sang to itself a joyous, an eternal song.

" Where do you want to go to ? " asked a voice. It was a voice imbued with helpfulness and not with idle curiosity.

" I have to go up to the hills," I said.

Now I knew all about the galaxy of lights that were encamped upon the lower and the middle slopes, for the same lights were dancing in my breast. What I must do was to attack the higher ground and plant among those mournful meadows and the dark woods an array of brilliant flowers—I had thousands of them to bestow.

" Will you not wait for me ? " exclaimed the voice.

Who was this man ? Well, he was overtaking me and I had scruples as to that. Maybe it is better not to travel than to meet and smile and say good-bye.

The cold air and these speculations had a sobering effect upon me. If I let the man go with me I would love him—I knew from his voice—then we would have to part. But at this juncture, when I was debating if it would be wise to shake him off, there came into my mind a sketch of half a man at Lány. In that castle of the President of the Republic there is an amusing picture of the literary and artistic coterie in which the President relaxes. In the centre of the group the venerable sage discourses, with a cigarette in a tremendously long holder. And the forefinger of his right hand is emphasising what he says, an attitude that was so popular among the prophets. Face to face with him is Karel Čapek with his forefinger identically raised. At the left of Masaryk is Dr. Beneš, Europe's record Foreign Minister, with an expression of incredible astuteness. Twelve or thirteen other personages are depicted and one angle of this work of art is occupied by the two legs of somebody from the knees downward. When a gentleman feels that he has been wrongfully omitted from the group and utters a complaint : " My dear fellow," says the artist, " those two legs belong to you."

Thus even half a man might be desirable. Yes, I would take up to the hills with me this comrade who was tramping in my wake. And if we stayed together only half an hour perhaps we would have memories that would stay for all the hours to come.

We passed the former palace of a former Austrian Archduke and we skirted the long wall behind which is the garden. Lovely trees waved to and fro. They were aware that after 1918 they had ceased to be Habs-burgian archiducal trees. I heard them whispering that they were trees of liberty. I heard—but did they say what they believed I would prefer to hear ?

In the long avenue ascending to the station there was very little traffic. Much more was the traffic in the sky, because the moon had risen and the sheet of greyness had dissolved into an archipelago of islands, floating, jostling islands which had small respect for one another. Then the moon swam into a wide, purple lake.

We crossed the railway line and up and up we went. At first the road was winding through a sort of park and presently we found ourselves in a steep lane. The other end of it was an uneven plateau. We looked down from there on Bratislava and the Danube. How could there be anything more beautiful than the mysterious town in that strange light ?

" Slovakia, Slovakia," I murmured.

" You think it is a happy land, a free land," my companion said. " Look at the Danube rolling out into the dark, the infinite."

" Who are you ? " I demanded.

" We live in a world so limited," he said, " a finite world and we are infinite. Thus we are barred from happiness. And every land on which the moon has fallen . . ."

" Do you mean," said I, " that they are all un-happy ? "

" They may have their virtues and their victories,"
quoth he. " Some lands attract us more than others.
But do you believe that they are happy ? "

" See," I answered, " what Slovakia has done since
the Republic came into the world."

" What is a land," said he, " but her inhabitants ?
Our greatness, for we have inherited a portion of the
infinite, will not allow us to be happy."

A dark bird—I could not see what kind of bird—was
fluttering overhead and evidently it was agitated.

" Do you make no difference," I asked, " between
one country and another ? "

" What we have to cherish most of . . . most of all,"
said he, " is . . ."

Little voices near our feet were calling to the bird
and with a cry of love and anguish it came swooping
down.

THE END